THE HERSCHELS OF HANOVER

In August 1731 a gardener-turned-musician named Isaac Herschel arrived in Hanover and joined the Hanoverian Guards as an oboist. A year later he married the illiterate Anna Moritzen, who was in service in the town and who was already pregnant by him.

Isaac and Anna were to have ten children, of whom six survived childhood. Their parents could provide them with little except a modest schooling and (for the four boys) teaching on the oboe and violin. Yet three of the boys entered the service of King George III as members of the Court Orchestra of the Elector of Hanover, while five grandsons played to the King at dinner in Windsor Castle as members of the band of Queen Charlotte.

In early middle age, the fourth boy — William Herschel — accepted King George's invitation to give up music and become astronomer to the Court at Windsor. William had already taught himself to make telescopes, and his 7-ft reflector was the finest in the land. With it he had made the sensational discovery of a new planet, and he was using it to collect double stars by the hundred, thereby introducing into astronomy the methodology of the natural historian that he had learned from his brother Dietrich. With help from his brother Alexander, William went on to become the premier manufacturer of large reflectors, and his 40-ft with a mirror weighing a ton was to appear on the Ordnance Survey map. With the invaluable assistance of his sister Caroline, the first salaried female astronomer in history, he surveyed the whole of the sky visible from Windsor and collected over 2500 nebulae and clusters of stars, thereby opening up these mysterious objects to scientific study. The very existence of clusters showed that attractive forces were at work in the heavens, and this implied that a cluster that today is scattered will in time — as it grows older — become more and more concentrated. Recognition of this led William to theorize boldly about the evolution of stars and star systems, so setting astronomy on the path to the science we know today, in which everything — even the universe itself — has a life history.

In their different ways, no fewer than ten of Isaac and Anna's immediate descendants were at one time or another in royal service. In a series of biographical sketches, this book tells the story of this extraordinary family.

THE HERSCHELS
OF HANOVER

Michael Hoskin

SCIENCE HISTORY PUBLICATIONS

Michael Hoskin is a Fellow of Churchill College, Cambridge, and Emeritus Fellow of St Edmund's College, Cambridge. His books on the Herschels include *William Herschel and the Construction of the Heavens*, *The Herschel Partnership*, and *Caroline Herschel's Autobiographies*, the last two being published by Science History Publications Ltd.

Published by Science History Publications Ltd
16 Rutherford Road, Cambridge, CB2 8HH
United Kingdom
www.shpltd.co.uk

First published 2007

Printed and bound in the United Kingdom by
University Printing, University Press, Cambridge

ISBN 978 0 905193 07 6

Contents

The Herschel Family

Isaac and Anna Herschel

Isaac was born 14 [not 4] Jan. 1707, Hohenziaz (now part of Magdeburg). Married ANNA ILSE [or ILSA] MORITZEN, 12 Oct. 1732, Schlosskirche, Hanover. Died 22 Mar. 1767, Hanover; buried in Gartenfriedhof. Anna was born late Dec. 1712 or early Jan. 1713, Neustadt am Rübenberge; died 19 Nov. 1789, Hanover, buried in same grave as Isaac (and, later, Caroline). Ten children, as follows.

Sophia Elizabeth Griesbach [Sophia; née Herschel]

Born 12 Apr. 1733, Hanover. Married bandsman JOACHIM HEINRICH GRIESBACH, 21 Jan. 1755, Hanover. Died 30 March 1803, Hanover (buried 3 April). Heinrich was born 23 July 1730, Bodenwerder; died 31 Jan. 1773, Coppenbrügge (buried 3 Feb.). Seven children:

GEORGE LUDOLPH JACOB GRIESBACH [GEORGE], born 11 Oct. 1757, Hanover (baptised 13 Oct.). Married his pupil MARY WRIGHT SMITH, 31 Oct. 1786, Windsor; nine children. Died 23 Nov. 1824, Windsor.

CARL FRIEDRICH LUDWIG GRIESBACH [CHARLES], born 5 Mar. 1760, Coppenbrügge. Married SARAH WIGG, 15 Dec. 1796, Medstead; ten children. Died 20 Mar. 1835, Pocklington, Yorks. Sarah was born on 8 July 1776 and died 1830 at Baden near Vienna, presumably on a tour.

JUSTUS HEINRICH CHRISTIAN GRIESBACH [HENRY], born 22 Apr. 1762, Coppenbrügge. Married (i) MARY BLAKENEY, 27 June 1791; five children. Mary was born 27 June 1764 and died 25 Jan. 1831. (ii) MARY BLOEMFIELD, 10 Oct. 1832. Henry died 9 Feb. 1833, Windsor.

ANNE ELEONORE CHARLOTTE GRIESBACH, born 17 Feb. 1764, Coppenbrügge. Died there (of smallpox), 17 Dec. 1766.

FRIDERICA WILHELMINA GRIESBACH, born 24 Feb. 1767, Coppenbrügge. Still living in Germany (unmarried) in 1825.

JOHANN FRIEDRICH ALEXANDER GRIESBACH [FREDERICK], born 2 June 1769, Coppenbrügge. Married MARY FRANCES WYBOROW, daughter of the first Master Cook at Windsor Castle, 16 Oct. 1792; eight children. Died 11 Jan. 1825 at Putney or Brompton.

JOHANN WILHELM GRIESBACH [WILLIAM], born 10 Jan. 1772, Coppenbrügge. Unmarried, one daughter.[1] Died 25 June 1825.

Heinrich Anton Jacob Herschel [Jacob]

Born 20 Nov. 1734, Hanover. Unmarried. Died (by strangulation), 23 June 1792, Hanover.

Johann Heinrich Herschel

Born 25 Apr. 1736, Hanover. Died 26 Oct. 1743, Hanover.

Friedrich Wilhelm Herschel [William]

Born 15 Nov. 1738, Hanover. Married Mrs MARY PITT, 8 May 1788, Upton Church. Died 25 Aug. 1822, Slough (buried in Upton Church). Mary was born 13 June 1750, the daughter of ADEE BALDWIN and his wife ELIZABETH (née BROOKER, died 22 October 1798). Mary's only sibling, THOMAS BALDWIN (1754–1821), had three children, including SOPHIA BALDWIN (who often accompanied William and Mary on their travels). Mary's first marriage was to JOHN PITT, who died late summer 1786; their son PAUL ADEE PITT died February 1793. Mary died 6 Jan. 1832, Slough (buried in Upton Church). One child:

JOHN FREDERICK WILLIAM HERSCHEL [JOHN], born 7 Mar. 1792, Slough. Married MARGARET BRODIE STUART ['Maggie'], 3 Mar. 1829, St Marylebone, London; twelve children. Died 11 May 1871, Hawkhurst, Kent (buried next to Newton in Westminster Abbey). 'Maggie' was born 16 Aug. 1810, died 3 Aug. 1884.

Anna Christina Herschel
Born Hanover, 12 or 13 July 1741. Died (of whooping cough), Hanover, 22 July 1748.

Johann Alexander Herschel [Alexander]
Born Hanover, 13 Nov. 1745. Married Mrs MARGARET SMITH, 31 July 1783, Walcot Church, Bath. No children. Died, Hanover, 16 Mar. 1821 (buried in Gartenfriedhof, 20 Mar.). Margaret died, Bath, *c.* 5 Feb. 1788 (buried at Weston, Bath, 10 Feb.).

Maria Dorethea Herschel
Born Hanover, 8 June 1748. Died Hanover, 21 Apr. 1749.

Carolina Lucretia Herschel [Caroline]
Born Hanover, 16 Mar. 1750. Died Hanover, 9 Jan. 1848. Buried in parents' grave in Gartenfriedhof, 18 Jan.

Frantz Johann Herschel
Born, Hanover, 13 May 1752. Died (of smallpox), 26 Mar. 1754.

Johann Dietrich Herschel [Dietrich]
Born Hanover, 13 Sept. 1755. Married CATHARINA MARIA REIFF, 5 Oct. 1779, Schlosskirche, Hanover. Died Hanover, 19 Jan. 1827 (buried in Neustaedter Hof- und Stadtkirche). Catharina was born, Hanover, 16 Jan. 1760, and died, Hanover, 1 Dec. 1846 (buried in Schlosskirche); she was the 2nd daughter of Georg Heinrich Reiff (1721 – 30 Dec. 1804) and Anna Elizabeth, *née* Lindemann (1717 – 5 Nov. 1788). Four children:

GEORG HEINRICH HERSCHEL, born Hanover 7 Mar. 1781 (baptised 15th). Died (of yellow fever), Charlestown, USA, *c.* 1805.

ANNA ELIZABETH HERSCHEL, born Hanover 17 June 1783 (baptised 22nd). Married CHRISTIAN PHILIPP KNIPPING, 30 July 1802. Nine children. Died Hanover, 4 Feb. 1872. Christian was born Hemeringen, 21 Jan. 1760; died Lachen, 2 July 1822.

SOPHIA DOROTHEA HERSCHEL, born Hanover 3 June 1785 (baptised 12th). Married Dr JOHANN FRIEDRICH WILHELM RICHTER, 3 Jan. 1809. Four children. Died 12 Jan. 1861. Johann died Feb. 1832.

CAROLINE WILHELMINE MARIE ANTONIE HERSCHEL, born Hanover 10 June 1799 (baptised 12th), still living June 1864. Married Dr GROSKOPFF; one son.

This information comes from numerous sources, including Isaac Herschel's autobiography; records in the Herschel Family Archives; records held by Anne Jarvis and Richard Leaver, whose families are descendants of Sophia Griesbach; letters from Caroline Herschel; and, especially, church records from Hanover, Coppenbrügge and Bath.

Preface

In recent centuries astronomy has profited from a number of remarkable partnerships. The Danzig brewer Johannes Hevelius (1611–87) and his second wife Elisabetha collaborated in measuring the angles separating pairs of stars; using an octant equipped with two sighting bars, Johannes would point one bar towards the first star while Elisabetha pointed the other bar towards the second, and they would then read off the angle between the bars from a graduated scale. Nearer our own time, the English astrophysicist William Huggins (1824–1910) and his wife Margaret joined forces to identify lines in the spectra of stars that revealed the chemical composition of the stars from which the light came.

But Elisabetha knew what awaited her when she married Johannes, as did Margaret when she married William: the collaborations were entered into by consenting adults. But the greatest partnership of all was between siblings: William, Caroline and Alexander Herschel. With a little help from their brother Dietrich, they changed the course of astronomical history. The eighteenth century had learned from Isaac Newton and Gottfried Wilhelm Leibniz that God was the great Clockmaker and the universe his masterpiece: planets eternally cycled in their orbits around the Sun as the cogs of a clock endlessly rotate, with the stars as a rarely-changing (and therefore uninteresting) backcloth. This is in complete contrast with astronomy today, in which the solar system is a minority pursuit, and where everything from a star to the cosmos itself has a life history.

This fundamental change in how astronomers view the universe was triggered by the Herschel partnership. Dietrich, an amateur entomologist, taught William to collect and classify butterflies, using the methods of the natural historian. William was fascinated by the faint and mysterious milky patches in the sky known as nebulae: very distant star clusters would of course appear nebulous, but were *all* nebulae distant star clusters? Using a telescope whose mirror had great 'light-gathering power', constructed in 1783 and perfected with the help of Alexander, and with Caroline sharing the night watches and ready to write down his shouted observations, he collected many hundreds of nebulae in a campaign that lasted two decades. For part of this time he believed that all his nebulae were star clusters, and he classified them according to the degree of clustering they displayed. But the very existence of clusters implied that attractive forces must be at work, presumably Newtonian gravitation: if so, stars were pulling each other into ever-closer embrace, and a widely scattered cluster would in time become more and more condensed. Clusters therefore went through a life-cycle, scattered clusters being young and condensed clusters old. Classifying his specimens of nebulae according to their age, William asked:

... is it not almost the same thing, whether we live successively to witness the germination, blooming, foliage, fecundity, fading, withering, and corruption of a plant, or whether a vast number of specimens, selected from every stage through which the plant passes in the course of its existence, be brought at once to our view?[1]

It would be decades before the community of professional astronomers shifted the focus of their attentions from the planets to the stars, and abandoned the clockwork model and replaced it with the quasi-biological view of the universe that we know today; but this passage encapsulates the revolution that the Herschel siblings set in train.

That four of the children of Isaac Herschel, a penniless bandsman in the Hanoverian Guards, and his illiterate wife Anna should be involved in this transformation of astronomy is a remarkable testimony to the family in which they were reared. But the family were first and foremost musicians. Late in the eighteenth century, when William was well established as astronomer to the Court at Windsor Castle, and King George III brought his guests to be shown the heavens by William and Caroline, these same guests had been serenaded at dinner by a band five of whose members were sons of Sophia, eldest daughter of Isaac and Anna. Sophia's brothers Jacob, Alexander and Dietrich were all at one time or another members of the Court orchestra in Hanover, of which George was Elector. And so it was that no fewer than ten of Isaac and Anna's immediate descendants entered the service of King George, as musicians or astronomers.

Anna taught her children the value of thrift and hard work; Isaac fostered their musical talents, and opened their eyes to the excitements that await the enquiring mind. This book tells the story of this most remarkable family, the Herschels of Hanover, in the form of biographical sketches of the parents and of each of their ten children.

The sketches of the parents, and of the children other than William and Caroline, attempt to be as complete as present knowledge allows. In the case of William and Caroline our sources are so extensive that completeness is not an attainable goal. From Caroline's pen we have a mountain of manuscripts, as well as two autobiographies; these were recently edited and published by the present writer, who has also written a book-length assessment of the great partnership as seen from her point of view. The sketch of Caroline therefore focuses on the key episodes in her life and refers the reader to these other publications as appropriate.

As to William, the definitive account of his 'life and works' that must one day be written will run to several volumes. These will of course concentrate on his astronomy, which is what is important to history. But we must not forget that until he was 43-years-old — that is, for the first half of his life — he was a professional musician who hoped to be remembered as a composer. Music was as important to him then as astronomy was later, and the present sketch therefore discusses at length his life as a musician, for this is probably unfamiliar even to a student of the Herschels. In writing of his extraordinary career in astronomy, we focus on the motive that drove him — his ambition to understand 'the construction of the heavens' — for this led to what we may term the Herschelian revolution in astronomy. William made many contributions to knowledge of the solar system, not least his discovery of the planet Uranus, but these were hardly revolutionary. It was by his investigations of our neighbours among the stars, and still more so by his exploration of the cosmos, that William set astronomy on a new path, and this is the subject of a concluding chapter.

The format adopted here has two drawbacks, for which the indulgence of the reader is requested. First, the biographical sketches are very different in length. This is unavoidable, for whereas Maria Dorethea lived only a few months and all we shall ever know about her can be said in a few lines, Caroline lived to the age of 97. Second, the lives of the parents and their ten children naturally overlapped. Thus when Caroline chose to leave Hanover to make a career in England, it affected her mother (who was promised an annuity to pay for substitute help in the house), the two brothers she left behind, and the two brothers she joined in Bath. The episode is therefore mentioned in all their biographical sketches, a duplication that seems unavoidable; but it is discussed at greater length in the sketch of Caroline, for she was the one most affected by the move.

I have benefitted from the generosity and helpfulness of numerous friends and colleagues. John Herschel-Shorland did everything possible to help, as he always does. Anthony Turner presented me with his complete store of Herschel materials. Arndt Latusseck, who lives near Hanover, was tireless in examining church records and exploring graveyards. Anne Jarvis, whose step-father was descended from Sophia Herschel, made available the manuscript memoir by Sophia's son George. Richard Leaver, another descendant from Sophia, put at my disposal a wealth of material from that side of the family. Emily Winterburn copied for me her copious notes on the store of Herschel materials in the British Library. Kenneth James, whose unpublished thesis is the primary source for the musical life in Bath in the Herschel era, put his knowledge at my disposal. And the William Herschel Society, through its Curator, Deborah James, made available on extended loan the original typescript of Constance Lubbock's heavily-edited *The Herschel Chronicle*. Lastly, my thanks to Bernard Hoskin for converting my electronic files into a book.

Isaac and Anna

For Isaac Herschel, education was the key to fulfilment in life. He had learnt this from his father; although no more than a humble gardener on an estate near Magdeburg, Abraham Herschel "was very fond of the art of arithmetic and writing as well as of drawing and music. Particularly in arithmetic and writing he achieved a high level".[1] We can picture Abraham returning home from his day of manual work, washing his hands, having supper, and then finding the energy and the intellectual curiosity to stretch his mind with pen and paper, to the wonderment of his son.

Isaac was the youngest of Abraham's four children.[2] Born on 14 January 1707 when his father was already in his late fifties, he was to have followed Abraham into horticulture; but Abraham died when Isaac was eleven, and his widow could not afford to pay for the usual apprenticeship. Nevertheless, the resourceful boy taught himself the rudiments of gardening, and eventually, with the help of his brother Eusebius, he got a position tending the garden of an aristocratic widow. This earned him his daily bread; but he felt an inner compulsion to be a musician, and nothing else would satisfy him. As a boy he had bought a violin and taught himself to play by ear; now he purchased an oboe, and used his wages to pay for lessons.

When he was twenty-one, Isaac took his courage in both hands, quit his job with the widow, and set off for Berlin to find a post as oboist — only to decide that what he was offered was "very bad and slavish".[3] So, with the financial support of Eusebius and their sister, he embarked on a year's musical training with an old Prussian band-conductor. Eusebius, however, for all his generosity, was not convinced that music offered a secure career, and he prevailed upon Isaac to come and live with him and learn husbandry. But the call of music proved too strong, and before long Isaac was again on his travels and looking for a post as oboist. He was offered a position in Brunswick, but it was "too Prussian". At Hanover however he found that the Guards band offered terms he was prepared to accept, and so on 7 August 1731 Isaac at last achieved his ambition and became a professional musician.[4]

After a year in the army, Isaac married Anna Ilse Moritzen, the teenage daughter of a baker of Neustadt am Rübenberge, some 40km northwest of Hanover.[5] Anna, who was born around 1 January 1713,[6] had three brothers and two sisters, and Isaac records for us details of their respective offspring.[7] No doubt his wife, coming as she did from a village in the country, was accustomed to large and settled extended families; and because Isaac had travelled so far from his birthplace and was rapidly losing touch with his family, "she might have imagined her husband had dropt from the clouds".[8]

It is likely that Anna was in Hanover because she was in domestic service there.

Like so many girls of her generation who had attended the village school, she could neither read nor write;[9] and she was to set no store on anything except housework and the rearing of children. Why Isaac, with his obsession for education, married Anna remained a mystery until the exact date of their marriage, 12 October 1732, was established: Anna was already pregnant with their first child. It is no surprise that a lonely bandsman should bed a young girl who for the first time was free from the constraints of home; thus were the foundations laid for the great Herschel dynasty. All the signs are that they married in haste, and the ceremony was held, not in the bride's home village, but in the relative anonymity of the Garrison Church in Hanover.[10]

Life for a bandsman was pleasant enough in times of peace. Isaac could live at home and foster the musical training — and the broader education — of their sons (the upbringing of the girls being in the hands of Anna). But in time of war he might well be away on campaign, and although the musicians of the band were allowed to take cover when the shooting started, they shared the privations of the troops.

In 1740, when the Herschel family consisted of a daughter and three sons, the War of the Austrian Succession broke out; and the following summer, about the time Isaac and Anna's second daughter was born, the Guards marched out of Hanover and went on campaign. In June 1743 Isaac was present at the Battle of Dettingen, and although the Hanoverians were victorious, he and his comrades spent the following night in a waterlogged field. Isaac lost the use of his limbs, and his health was never to recover. He was taken to Wiesbaden for convalescence; and later he was granted a spell of sick-leave at home, one consequence of which was the birth in November 1745 of their fourth son, Alexander.[11]

In October 1743, Anna had had the distressing duty of informing her absent husband of the death of their second son, Johann Heinrich, then seven years old, of whom he had been "doatingly fond".[12] Not surprisingly, Isaac soon became totally disenamoured of army life, and when the regiment finally returned to Hanover on 13 February 1746 he successfully applied for 'dismission'.[13] But how was he now to earn a living? He was no church organist; and although Hanover was the home of the Court Orchestra of the Elector, Isaac's modest musical abilities did not allow him to aspire so high. And so the following winter he decided to move his family to the vicinity of Hamburg, a major city where surely there would be openings for a musician.[14]

To his dismay

> ... on his arrival there, he was much disappointed at finding Music in too low an estimation, compared to what he had been used to in Hanover, where it always was much encouraged, and an excellent Orchestra at the Court kept up, and therefore a place more likely to afford the desired improvement to [his sons].[15]

Late in 1747, while he pondered what best to do, Isaac chanced to meet a former pupil, General Georg August von Wangenheim, no less. Evidently the general had a great respect and affection for Isaac. The prospects for peace, he assured him, were good, and so if Isaac rejoined the Hanoverian Guards he could expect years in which he could live contentedly at home with his wife and children. Not only that, but his talented eldest son Jacob — born in 1734, and just thirteen years of age — would forthwith become a wage-earning bandsman alongside his father, and his second surviving son, William, born in 1738, might expect to do the same when he left school.[16]

It was a proposal that solved all Isaac's problems at a stroke. On 11 December 1747 the Herschels returned to Hanover,[17] and Isaac was soon using his sons' wages to extend their education with lessons in French and, for William if not for Jacob, in mathematics and various branches of philosophy.[18] The heroic scale of the intellectual curiosity that Isaac, despite his humble origins and equally humble circumstances, could foster in a teenage son is revealed for us by his youngest daughter Caroline:

> But generally their conversation would branch out on Philosophical subjects, when my brother W^m and his Father often were arguing with such warmth and my Mother's interference became necessary when the names Leibnitz, Newton and Euler sounded rather too loud for the repose of her little on[es]; who ought to be in school by seven in the morning. But it seems that on the brothers' retiring to their own room, where they partook of one bed, my brother W^m had still a great deal to say; and frequently it happened that when he stopt for an assent or reply; he found his hearer [Jacob] was gone to sleep, and I suppose it was not till then when he bethought himself to do the same.[19]

Sadly, this happy state of affairs was not to last. In the winter of 1755/6 France began to threaten both Great Britain and the Electorate of Hanover, which were united under King George II, and the Hanoverian Guards were mobilized. Isaac, Jacob and William took their places in the band alongside Heinrich Griesbach, the husband of Isaac's eldest daughter Sophia (b. 1733), and marched away. Before long they were summoned overseas to reinforce the defences of England, where they arrived in April.[20]

At a stroke Anna's family had been deprived of all four of its menfolk, and Anna was left with Alexander, Caroline (b. 1750) and little Dietrich (b. 1755) in her sole charge; and although Sophia moved back home, she was a doubtful asset, both financially and emotionally. Isaac arranged for Anna to have half his pay and that of their two bandsman sons; Sophia's husband simply assumed her mother would support her.[21] Meanwhile Anna, being illiterate, depended on others to write her letters, and little Caroline acted as scribe for her (and for other soldiers' wives) when she was only eight or nine years old.[22]

In England Jacob, who aspired to membership of the Hanoverian Court Orchestra, obtained dismission from the army, and returned home a civilian. Isaac, William and Heinrich arrived in Hanover with the band in January 1757;[23] but they were with their families for only a few months before the Guards were again on the march, and this time the threat was against Hanover itself. On 26 July 1757 the Hanoverians and their allies were defeated at the Battle of Hastenbeck.[24] Isaac eventually told both Jacob and William to seek refuge in England, while he himself, a grown man under oath, was obliged to suffer the hardships of a defeated army (and a brief period of arrest following the desertion of William[25]).

Under the Convention (or Capitulation) of Klosterzeven the Hanoverian troops were exiled and the town itself occupied by the French.[26] Enemy troops were billeted in the very house where Anna and her children had their apartment.[27] After six months the occupiers were ousted from Hanover, and Anna was then able to supplement her income by doing needlework for a friend who had the commission of supplying the army with tents and linen.[28] Her ailing husband and her two eldest sons were away, Sophia had moved to Coppenbrügge with Heinrich and their three-months-old son, and Alexander was living with them as apprentice to Heinrich; and so there was no one to help care for Caroline and Dietrich. Small wonder that the stressed Anna's "way of treating children was rather severe".[29]

Campaigning continued into the summer of 1759, when at long last the French were defeated at the Battle of Minden and expelled from the region.[30] Even so, it was not until the following May, after an absence of nearly three years, that Isaac was at last able to return to his family, a civilian once more, but broken in health.[31]

Jacob had by now returned again from England and successfully auditioned for a place in the Court Orchestra, but William was technically a deserter living abroad. Only in March 1762 did Isaac — or, more likely, Jacob — obtain for him his formal dismission.[32] It was another two years before William visited Hanover, and was able to reassure his father as to his future prospects in his adopted country.[33]

That August Isaac suffered a paralytic seizure that left him temporarily speechless and deaf. He struggled on, doing what he could to support his family, until at the end of February 1767 he was confined to bed. Three weeks later, on 22 March, he died.[34] He was buried in the Gartenfriedhof.[35]

Isaac left his family in poverty, having refused in his final weeks to connive in a fraudulent declaration of good health.[36] Yet musically and intellectually the legacy he left was most remarkable for a man whose formal education had been minimal. Caroline records a number of incidents that show that when Isaac's military duties took him away from his family in Hanover, his greatest regret was the damage his absence did to the education of his children. In Isaac's first campaign, when William was little more than a toddler, "I heard [William] mentioned by my Mother as one of the children she had to look to, that their practice was not to be neglected".[37] And when Isaac returned home from his last campaign and was greeted by his youngest child, Dietrich, then just four years old,

> on the same evening before he [Isaac] went to rest, the Adempken (a small Violin) was taken from the lumbering shelf, and newly strung, and the dayly Lessons immediately commensed....[38]

It was fortunate that Isaac's happiest years — the decade between his first dismission early in 1746 and the mobilization of the Guards in the winter of 1755/6 — were also the years of William's late childhood and adolescence, when the admirable example of his father could be decisive. Caroline regrets that war then interrupted William's "philosophical pursuits", for otherwise "we should have had much earlier proofs of his inven[t]ful genius". In this connection she mentions Isaac's interest in astronomy, though it appears to have amounted to little more than an acquaintance with some constellations and a knowledge of where to engrave the equator and ecliptic on a celestial globe.[39] In matters of the mind Isaac stimulated rather than instructed his sons. Little could he have imagined where the arguments over Leibnitz, Newton and Euler would eventually lead.

Both before and after the death of her husband, Anna did all she could to prevent Caroline acquiring skills that would enable her to leave home and find work elsewhere. Yet Caroline could be remarkably understanding: Anna, she says, acted from "an erroneous though well meant opinion ... for it was her certain belief; my brother Wilhelm [William] would have returned to his Country, and my eldest brother [Jacob] not have looked so high, if they had had a little less learning".[40]

As it turned out, Caroline eventually made good her escape from Hanover in 1772, after William invited her to join him in Bath (placating Anna by arranging an annuity to pay for substitute help in the house).[41] Thereafter Anna largely disappears from our story. But a solitary letter from her survives, albeit in imperfect format — as dictated to Dietrich and later translated into English by Anna's great-grand-daughter. Evidently one of the two sons of Sophia who were already musicians in the Queen's band at Windsor had written to Hanover with news of William's appointment in the summer of 1782 as astronomer to the Court at Windsor, William having neglected to do so. No doubt Anna's letter was 'improved' by both Dietrich and the translator, but it nevertheless reveals a more lively and intelligent mind than one might have expected:

Dear Son
 I must at last really break through the long silence, for it seems as if you had entirely forgotten that pen & ink can be used for any other purpose than to write astronomical observations. You must not expect anything new from my writing, as you know already that Heaven still grants me good health, but I think my dear William is not unwilling to hear that over again. A letter from Griesbach informs us that the King has made you his Astronomer & that you are leaving Bath; it is most agreeable news for me as now you can live for the remainder of your days without care, although you will be no Croesus as regards riches. To your sister Caroline also it will no doubt be pleasant, as she will be near the Griesbachs and so will have the opportunity of talking to her friends.
 As soon as you are settled, my dear son, write to me once how this change of yours has come about [*or* gone off], & whether your circumstances

will allow you to send me money as usual. I have arranged with Jacob that he pays me every quarter the 25 [thalers] and he receives it back from you & Alex when it comes. For the courier comes so irregularly, that I cannot well wait without getting into difficulties. Could you not arrange through Herr Wiese,[42] that the money should be paid out here each time & so Jacob would not have to be troubled, however I leave this to you. But if you wish to do me a favour do write just once to Jacob, he has written 6 letters & received no answer: I think some must have been lost. As my Sec[y] [Dietrich] has something to write about himself I will leave some space for him and only assure you how truly I am your devoted Mother.[43]

We next hear of Anna from a letter written by Jacob early in 1786: "She is still well and cheerful after her fashion, but yet certainly very weak and does not leave her room."[44] That summer she seems to have improved; for when William and Alexander called to see her in July on their way to Göttingen, William reported to Caroline that "Mama is perfectly well and looks well".[45] She died three years later, on 19 November 1789, aged 76 years and 10 months,[46] and was buried in the Gartenfriedhof alongside her husband.[47]

Sophia

Sophia Elizabeth, the eldest of Isaac and Anna's ten children, was born in Hanover on 12 April 1733, just six months after her parents' marriage. She has hitherto remained a shadowy figure because of the limited contact she had with her much younger sister Caroline, the family's chronicler; but new information on her and her family has recently come to light, in the form of the memoirs written by her eldest son George, along with the family records proudly preserved by her descendants, and information gleaned from church records both at Hanover and at nearby Coppenbrügge[1] where she lived in her middle years.[2]

Like all her siblings to come, Sophia attended the Garrison School, where she would have been taught reading, writing and religious studies, but not arithmetic, since she was a girl. Schooling normally ended at the age of fourteen, and this passage of life was marked by Confirmation; and no doubt Sophia was among the group who undertook this rite at Easter 1733. Caroline enviously portrays her eldest sister as having "the advantage before us yonger children of receiving a good education and being instructed in all branches of needlework",[3] and this instruction must have occupied Sophia in the months after she left school. By the time that Caroline was old enough to be conscious of her surroundings, her sister had for several years been in service as a lady's maid in a family at Brunswick.[4]

Presumably Sophia met her future husband, Joachim Heinrich Griesbach (23 July 1730[5] – 31 January 1773[6]), on a visit to her parents in Hanover, for Heinrich was a comrade of Sophia's father and brothers in the band of the Hanoverian Guards. Their courtship was conducted by correspondence, and Caroline declares disapprovingly that Heinrich's written endearments did not come from him but were composed by a friend for payment.[7] She also tells us that their father was opposed to the marriage, holding Heinrich to be a poor musician and a poorer prospect as a son-in-law.[8]

In fact Heinrich came from what would once have been described as a 'good' family, and this must be why Caroline speaks of him as "a man with much better prospects of maintaining a wife and family than my father ever had".[9] The Griesbachs[10] traced their ancestry back to the Middle Ages. In the mid-sixteenth century Bernardus Stevenus Ignatius De Griesbach had been born at the castle of Griesbach near Passau in Upper Austria, and his descendent Johann Daniel, born about 1630 in Wildemann, became a physician and surgeon and practised in Einbeck and then in Bodenwerder, a few miles from Coppenbrügge. His son, Stephan Bernhard Ignaz (1667–?), was likewise a surgeon in Bodenwerder, as was his son Johann Daniel (1696–1761). Johann Daniel married twice, and had six children from his first marriage and four from his second.[11]

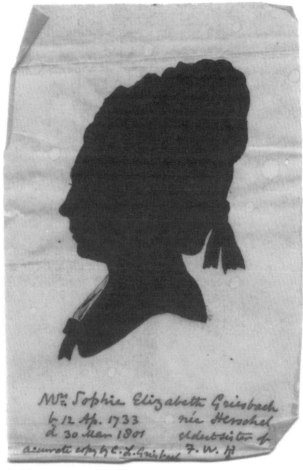

Sophia, as portrayed in a silhouette in the Herschel Family Archives.

It was the fourth son by Johann Daniel's first marriage who was to wed Sophia. The wedding took place in Hanover on 21 January 1755.[12] Isaac's family, Caroline tells us, were hard put to it to provide the expected entertainment, and Jacob and William Herschel found it necessary to draw two months' pay in advance for the purpose;[13] perhaps Isaac's misgivings stemmed in part from a feeling that Sophia was marrying above herself. The records give no hint as to why "Joachim Heinrich De Griesbach Doctor of Music" (if the family tree in the possession of his descendants is to be believed) occupied the lowly position of a bandsman in the Guards, but he may have been one of the less able members of the Griesbach family.

Heinrich's army duties required him to live in Hanover, and in the first months

Silhouettes of five of the six of Sophia's children who survived childhood, courtesy of the Herschel Family Archives and Anne Jarvis.

of their married life he and Sophia occupied an apartment in the same house as Sophia's parents. And so it was that the two families shared the alarm on 1 November 1755, when the great earthquake that devastated Lisbon also shook far-away Hanover.[14] And when the Guards marched out of Hanover soon thereafter on their way to reinforce England, Heinrich departed in company with Isaac, Jacob and William, having moved Sophia and their chattels back into her parents' home.[15]

Heinrich returned with the regiment to Hanover in January 1757,[16] and he and Sophia moved back into their own apartment. But in May 1757, with Sophia now pregnant, the Guards again marched out of Hanover to campaign against the French, and this time to suffer defeat at Hastenbeck. Within weeks — on 11 October 1757[17] — Sophia gave birth to Georg Ludolph Jacob (later known as George). His uncle Jacob, who was in hiding from the occupying troops, emerged briefly to stand as godfather at his christening at the Garrison Church.[18]

Isaac was to be separated from his family until May 1760, an unwilling absence of three full years. Yet somehow Heinrich managed to secure early dismission from the Guards, and he arrived in Hanover on 7 January 1758, when the French forces were still in occupation of the town.[19]

Either before his arrival or immediately thereafter,[20] Heinrich was appointed to the post of Town Musician (Stadtpfeifer,[21] or Stadtmusicus according to Caroline) of Coppenbrügge, having no doubt learned of the vacancy from his family in nearby Bodenwerder. The post was little more than a sinecure, and Heinrich received payment in corn (though Caroline's jaundiced memory was to see it as "a settlement which afforded good cheer and plenty",[22] no doubt because he had the right to play for private functions in the area). He was employed jointly by the town council and the church, and his duties included: arranging for hymn tunes to be played on the clarionet and sackbut twice a day from the church steeple, providing a group of violins to perform in church on great festivals when the *Te Deum* was sung, and playing the trumpet from the Town Hall on the morning of New Year's Day. He was expected to take apprentices, one of whom would perform alongside him from the church steeple. Heinrich supplemented his income with "the business of three other places in the Brunswick territory". He also made snuff.[23]

When Heinrich was organizing the removal of Sophia and their son George from Hanover, the eldest male resident in the Herschel household was Alexander, aged just twelve and with no one to supervise his musical practice. Normally Alexander would have remained a pupil at the Garrison School until he was fourteen. But for all his misgivings over Heinrich, Isaac saw his son-in-law as the only available teacher for Alexander, and so the boy became Heinrich's first apprentice. He was to live with the Griesbachs until he completed his studies in the spring of 1764.

When the post of teacher in the girls' school at Coppenbrügge fell vacant, Sophia successfully applied, and she remained in post while raising her family.[24] In addition to George, the Griesbachs had four sons and two daughters: Carl Friedrich Ludwig, later known as Charles, was born on 5 March 1760; Justus Heinrich Christian (Henry) on 22 April 1762;[25] Anne Eleonore Charlotte on 17 February

1764 (she was to die of smallpox on 17 December 1766, in an epidemic that cost Charles an eye[26]); Friderica Wilhelmina on 24 February 1767 (we hear no more of her, except that she was living in Germany, far from Hanover, in 1825[27] and was to die unmarried[28]); Johann Friedrich Alexander (Frederick) on 2 June 1769; and Johann Wilhelm (William) on 10 January 1772. A year later, at the age of forty-two, their father died (Caroline says he "perhaps shortened his days by excess of drinking"[29]), leaving his widow with five sons and a surviving daughter. Heinrich's debts were paid by William and Alexander Herschel.[30]

During all this childbearing, Sophia had continued to run the school. George remembered her as "a very clever and intelligent woman, esteemed and beloved by us all, and by all the first-rate people in Coppenbrügge".[31] She "acquitted herself to the satisfaction of everybody during perhaps 11 or 12 years, but so worrying and fatiguing it proved to her, that on the death of my Father she resigned".[32] The children were left "as it were, mere orphans, very little provided for, and hardly anything before us but misery".[33] Fortunately the citizens of Coppenbrügge allowed the widowed Sophia to retain the post of Stadtpfeifer for her sons, and George was the first incumbent since he alone was of an age to leave school.[34] As a child he had shown the family's usual precocious talent for music, and when only five was being made to perform for visitors on a small violin. The one teacher he had had throughout his schooling was a close friend of his father's, who had done everything he could to encourage the boy's musical development. George played the violin, cello, clarinet, oboe, French horn, sackbut, trumpet and piano; he gave lessons on the piano while still a teenager, and deputized for church services when necessary. And so the widow and her six children survived the next four years.

Once more, the talent for music displayed by the Herschel/Griesbach menfolk, and the international character of this profession, came to the rescue. For all his failings, Jacob, as head of the Herschel family following the death of their father Isaac, was always quick to exert himself on behalf of siblings in need; and so when an emissary arrived in Hanover from England in 1777 with a commission from King George III to recruit a band of musicians, he immediately bethought him of Sophia's eldest son (and his own godson), then almost twenty years of age. George was a shy boy, and no doubt had few musicians among his contemporaries in Coppenbrügge; and he had found his later 'teens difficult years. He was accordingly delighted when the letter arrived from his Uncle Jacob, who promised Sophia he would see that George was appointed if he was willing to accept such a post, as indeed he was.[35]

In his memoirs George tells in great detail of his journey to England in April/May 1778 and of the gracious reception accorded him and his fellows by the King and Queen. George was to be a member of Queen Charlotte's little band of some eight or so players. They must have presented a colourful spectacle:

> We soon received our uniform: plain scarlet coat, waistcoat and breeches, a cocked hat and sword, all which we wore whenever we stirred out of doors,

this being the order. To our great surprise we soon after that had a laced suit, with a cocked hat with a gold lace and the inside of the rim lined with red feathers.[36]

George was soon on the lookout for the possibility of recruiting some of his brothers to join him. Charles, second eldest of the brothers, had replaced George as Stadtpfeifer at Coppenbrügge and was unavailable,[37] but George persuaded his mother to send Henry to Hanover for lessons from a cellist in the Court Orchestra. Luckily for Henry, the cellist in the orchestra at Windsor was dismissed for dissolute conduct in the summer of 1779, and George successfully proposed that Henry should take his place.[38]

After a while Sophia began to hanker after the company of her mother and siblings in Hanover,[39] and so she secured Charles a post in the band of the Hanoverian Guards and moved back there with her other children early in the summer of 1785.[40] George tells us that, with Charles's pay from the Guards and money sent by her sons in England, she was well provided for. When William Herschel visited Hanover in July 1786, he reported to Caroline that "In Sophy there is hardly any change but a few white hairs on her head".[41] That year, George obtained a post in Queen Charlotte's band for Frederick (who was aged sixteen or seventeen), and then, in the early months of 1788, for William (aged sixteen).[42]

This left Charles the only son still at home. Not surprisingly, he soon began to envy his four brothers who were spending their time in the comfort and elegance of royal palaces. King George was evidently a kindly and caring employer, and when the brothers petitioned for Charles to join them, the King "seemed to sympathise with him, and he soon was here".[43] And so, by 12 October 1788,[44] all five of Sophia's sons were in the royal service at Windsor, as indeed were their uncle William and aunt Caroline at nearby Slough. Their mother was to live in Hanover until her death on 30 March 1803.[45]

Jacob

We have inherited two conflicting portraits of Heinrich Anton Jacob, second of Isaac and Anna's ten children and their eldest son. Born on 20 November 1734, he was four years older than William. Musically the most gifted of a highly talented family, he was in William's eyes a performer to be admired and when necessary indulged; and although Jacob was without intellectual ambitions of his own, he served a valued function as the sounding-board for his younger brother's adolescent pretentions in philosophy, science, and especially the theory of harmonics. To his sister Caroline, however, Jacob was a domineering brother sixteen years her senior, who after the death of their father became the family head to whom she owed an almost feudal allegiance and who treated her as a skivvy.

Jacob's penchant for seeing the world exclusively from his own viewpoint displayed itself when he was only eleven or so. Isaac was away with the regiment, frustrated at being unable to foster the education of his eldest son as he would have wished. All the Herschel children attended the simple lessons at the Garrison School, but somehow Isaac contrived an opening for Jacob that Caroline describes as "something similar to the Foundation at Eton",[1] where education of a wholly superior sort was on offer. It would have been sufficient to allow Jacob to enter the Church if he so wished; alternatively, he would have been given training on the organ that might lead to a career as a cathedral organist.

Which school this was, and how Isaac managed to pull the necessary strings while away on campaign, are mysteries, but the outcome was that Jacob was given the opportunity to advance himself into the professional classes. We can imagine Isaac's dismay when he learned that his son, having been subjected to the usual teasing on his first day at the new school, had taken it "as an outrage against his dignity, returned home and nothing could induce him to go a second time".[2] It was back to the 'reading, writing and arithmetic' of the Garrison School for Jacob,[3] although Isaac arranged for his friend Lohman, organist of the Market Church in Hanover, to give the boy instruction on the clavier and organ "for not neglecting his practice entirely".[4]

Isaac obtained dismission from the army in the winter of 1745/6, but before long accepted the advice of General Wangenheim to rejoin. Although in late December 1747 Jacob was barely thirteen, he became a boy oboist in the Guards alongside his father.[5] In the years of peace that followed, Isaac was at home to foster the education of his sons. Lohman continued to teach Jacob the clavier and organ, and this bore fruit in 1753 when Jacob won a part-time appointment as organist for the new organ in the Garrison Church.[6] In the same year William too joined the Guards,[7] and the wages his sons were earning enabled Isaac to buy them lessons in French.[8] Despite the gap of four years in their ages, William was able to master the language more easily than his older brother, "who esteemed (I might almost say) Music as the only Science worthy of cultivation".[9]

Jacob and William were by now "oftens introduced as Solo performers and assistants in the Orchester of the Court",[10] while the post of organist no doubt gave Jacob further opportunities to display his musical talent; and in the winter of 1755/6 he was assured of one of the coveted places in the Hanoverian Court Orchestra. Unfortunately the monarch was resident in England, and so it was from England that confirmation of Jacob's appointment had to come,[11] after which his dismission from the Guards would be a formality. Unfortunately, the Guards were even then being summoned to reinforce England against the French, and it was touch-and-go as to whether the document from England would arrive in time. It did not, and a disgruntled Jacob found himself forced to prepare for a military campaign:

> preparations for marchin [were] going forward in which my Father found it almost impossible to satisfy my Brother Jacob who was spoiled by indulgien-cies, and now not only saw himself on the point of being separated from all his ease and Nickenackes but to be obliged to carrie all necessaries about his person. I [Caroline] was present at one of these altercations when my Father came home with 3 pair of Pocket Knifs & Forks of equal value, of which my brother Jacob had the choice, but he declared he could not carrie them, and I saw my Father was made very angery.[12]

As Jacob was on military service in England and so unavailable for the Court Orchestra, the place was given to another musician; and (as is the way of things) only then did Jacob receive dismission.[13] He returned home by carriage, a civilian at last, leaving his father and brother to follow on foot in due course along with the regiment.

Jacob now had to earn a living.

> My eldest brother was now unsettled. Of teaching he was never fond, most of his time he spent in composing; but this also was never turned to account for no printer could offer him high enough, nor would he let a piece (to my knowledge) be performed any where without he was directing. And having an immoderate passion for show and appearing grand, my Father and brother W^m undoubtedly suffered great privations when in England on his account, so that he might return with cloathing of English manufactory and Tayloring ... for Jacob had ever been loved, and too much admired for his musical and other promising abilities, by both; to deney him any gratification; but on this occasion my Father became almost disgusted with his extravagant fancies....[14]

Before long, however, such family problems were overshadowed by the threat of the French against Hanover, and in July 1757 the Hanoverian troops were defeated at Hastenbeck. Isaac and William were away in the field, but Jacob was at home and at risk of being pressed into the makeshift force being hastily assembled for the defence of Hanover. His sense of public duty was minimal, and he went into hiding:

> My brother keeping himself so carefully from all notice was undoubtedly to avoid the danger of being pressed, for all unengaged young men were forced in the service. Even the Clergy without they had livings were not exempted.[15]

After the French occupied the city, and soldiers were billetted in the very house where the Herschels lived, Jacob, as an able-bodied Hanoverian, now had a different but equally compelling reason to avoid being noticed. He emerged from hiding only on 13 October, to stand as godfather to Sophia's firstborn George.[16]

Soon after, Isaac somehow got word to Jacob urging him to flee Hanover and join William in Hamburg, so that the brothers might seek refuge in England. To raise the necessary funds, Isaac used his credit with an agent whose family included some of his pupils.[17]

> When we arrived in London [William later wrote] we made use of the recommendation of some of the families we had been known to when we were in England before. We were introduced to some private Concerts, my brother attended some scholars, and I copied music, by which means we contrived to live pretty comfortably in the winter, and in the summer we visited some families in and near Maidstone and Rochester and had a concert at Tunbridge Wells.[18]

Their struggle to survive was not helped by Jacob's high opinion of his own abilities as a musician. He declined to play 'second fiddle', considering it a "degradation" to perform unless he was himself first violin. Indeed, he simply refused to do so, even if this meant going hungry; and so the long-suffering William found himself helping to support his older brother.[19] Jacob's strategy evidently paid off, for after the final liberation of the region around Hanover he was (subject to an audition) offered the post of first violin in the Hanoverian Court orchestra.[20] Jacob "accordingly left [England] to go and, as was the custom, to play for the place, which he did the 15th of Octr".[21] But in order to pay for the passage home he had had once more to ask William for financial help, his younger brother "parting with his last farthing for travelling expenses".[22]

The audition successfully negotiated, in January 1760 Jacob found himself employed in what was an official residence of the reigning (though absent) sovereign, and entitled to entry into all strata of society, with the exception of the nobility, who formed a class apart. As a 'titled person', he "held his head very high, and expected his mother and sister to feel honoured by waiting on him".[23]

Jacob was now the principal breadwinner. Not only that, but Isaac's regiment was still away on campaign, and in his absence Jacob was the effective head of the family. Anna assumed he would be satisfied with sharing the same inexpensive accommodation as in past years; but within days of his arrival Jacob had moved out and taken a better apartment, where he was looked after by his landlord's servant. The rest of the family were to move to rooms in the same house, but these would not be vacant until Easter. Meanwhile Jacob returned home for his dinners; but according to Caroline these were far from pleasant occasions. No doubt the illiterate Anna grated on her son who was now moving in high society. Certainly Jacob's profligacy grated on Anna: when Anna went to visit Sophia she arranged for a neighbour to do the cooking, but Jacob insisted on having his meals fetched from a tavern at considerable expense.[24]

In May 1760 Isaac returned home at last after a three years' absence, but broken in health and in no state to impose sense on his eldest son. Jacob continued to dine at home, but the rest of his meals "were served up to him in style" in his own apartment.[25]

> ... my eldest Brother [Caroline was to write] (in the whole an excellent and sensible creature) was incorigible where Luxury, ease and Ostentation were in the case, And when He received his salary it was brought to his Mother, who was to keep house and provide for all and everything even his pocket money; and generally the Reciets were not enough to pay his Taylors bills &c., much less for the entertainements which were given to his Collegias and their Ladies when he had a Quartet party where his new Overtures and other compositions were tried and admired, which my Father expected and hoped would be turned to some profit by publishing them; but there was no printer who bid high enough, and nothing was published![26]

His family saw little of him, "for his whole attention was engrossed by two Lady Scholars for upwards of 4 years".[27] Eventually Jacob became engaged to a Fräulein Westenholtz, but for some reason this lady insisted they should quit Hanover and live elsewhere. This would require Jacob to resign from the Court Orchestra, and this he was unwilling to do, so to Isaac's relief the engagement, an "unequal connection", was broken off.

> Shee married in a pet an Old Gentelman. Left Hannover. Soon repented, and her name was mentioned no more in our Family.
> ... but in the hope that my brother would now go on more rationally [Isaac] was soon disapointed, for, Jacob was too fond of society, and if not engaged abroad could not spend an afternoon without having company at hom and unfortunately he associated only with families who lived in the most luxurious stile which in our circumstances it was impossible to receive them with any credit to ourselves.[28]

Not only that, but the two apartments were so close that Isaac and family had to keep quiet when Jacob had company; and if this meant that Dietrich had to miss his music lesson, so be it.

But there was another side to Jacob, one that the members of his family resident in Hanover barely glimpsed. William, taking his first steps in the intellectual life, needed a sympathetic listener, a sounding-board for his ideas, and Jacob willingly fulfilled this role:

> Before my brother left England [William later wrote] we made an agreement to carry on a regular correspondence, by means of a friend in London, who being in a public office, could send or receive our letters twice a week to and from Hanover free of postage. My brother being an excellent Musician and eminent composer, and also fond of intelligent disquisitions, my letters to him were chiefly relating to music; they also contained an account of my situation and circumstances, with occasional moral and metaphysical dissertations.[29]

The letters were written in the years 1761–63. Jacob carefully preserved them, and when William visited Hanover in 1764 he took them back, in the hope that they might one day appear in print.[30]

Before Isaac died early in 1767, he committed the musical upbringing of Dietrich to the care of Jacob.[31] But William had recently established himself in Bath, where his growing network of contacts offered his brothers the possibility of profitable visits to the town. Jacob could not resist the temptation, and in June he took leave from the Court Orchestra and set off, leaving Dietrich's training in the hands of Alexander.[32] At the performances of *Messiah* that inaugurated the organ of Bath's Octagon Chapel that October, it was Jacob who played the instrument.[33] But after a year, Jacob's conscience began to prick him, and he summoned Dietrich to Bath.[34] Anna however was worried that the boy had gone out into the world before he had been confirmed, and before long insisted on his return.[35] But Jacob had shrewdly dedicated a set of sonatas to Queen Charlotte, wife of King George III, and according to the established tradition of patronage he was due some pecuniary reward. He was therefore expecting a summons from the King, and meanwhile he must remain in England.

His performance at Court went so well that the King gave instructions for his salary from the Hanoverian Court Orchestra to be increased.[36] This was the first time that the monarch had encountered the Herschel family, but it would not be the last.

Jacob returned home with Dietrich in July 1769.[37] "So many luxurious fashions all at once were introduced" to meet Jacob's requirements that a servant had to be engaged to help cope.[38] A year later Jacob returned to Bath, this time with Alexander; but his visit was so brief — they left in July and Jacob was back by the autumn — that its chief purpose was no doubt to see Alexander safely there.

Jacob's concern for his brothers did not extend to the females in the family home. Anna and Jacob were forever at each other's throats, and Caroline bore the brunt of their displeasure. She "began to feel great anxiety about my future destination",[39] for when Jacob married he would have no further use for her services. Advised by Alexander,[40] William plotted her rescue, and in October 1771 he wrote to Jacob suggesting she join him in Bath to see if she could make a career as a singer; perhaps Jacob would help her make a start, by giving her lessons.[41] "This at first", Caroline writes dryly, "seemed to be agreeable to all parties, but by the time I had set my heart upon this change in my situation Jacob began to turn the whole scheeme into ridicule".[42] William however pressed matters to a conclusion by descending in person on Hanover in August 1772, at a time when it chanced that Jacob was away with the Court Orchestra, attending on the Queen of Denmark at a royal hunting lodge some eighty miles from Hanover. Jacob was vexed that he could take no part in the decision as to Caroline's future, his letters expressing "nothing but regret and impations at being thus disappointed".[43] Caroline was strangely loathe to leave without his permission, but a decision could not be delayed. And so she left, "without taking the consent to my going from my eldest brother along with me".[44]

With Caroline's departure to England we begin to lose track of Jacob, and we hear little of him until 1786. William had been commanded by the King to go in person to Göttingen and present a telescope to the university. Alexander would accompany him, and they were to take the opportunity to visit their family in Hanover. Jacob wrote to William on 27 February expressing delight at the forthcoming visit. He adds:

> I, for my part, am well, and my way of living as monotonous as my letters to you must be. Habit has grown upon me so that I am quite content without wish for change.
>
> Music is still my chief occupation; it is a pity that one must diligently follow it without hope of reward. However, if I once get the post of Concert-director, I shall be content. I already do the work as Verzin cannot on account of his age.[45]

But he was to be disappointed, for at his death six years later he was described as "Vice-Konzertmeister".[46]

William had not seen Jacob for fourteen years, and he reported to Caroline that he "looks a little older but not nearly so much as I expected".[47] The siblings resident in England were to meet their eldest brother just one more time, during Jacob's visit to that country from April to October 1787.[48] Thereafter there is silence, until a surviving letter from Dietrich to William in 1793 concerning the distribution of his estate.[49] Jacob had met a tragic end, found strangled on 23 June 1792 in a field outside the gates of Hanover.[50]

Johann Heinrich

Johann Heinrich, the third of Isaac and Anna Herschel's children, was born on 25 April 1736. Five years later Isaac's regiment became involved in the War of the Austrian Succession, and as a result, writes Caroline,

> My Father was obliged to leave my Mother with her little family, of whom the eldest son [Jacob] was between 6 and 7 and the next [Johann Heinrich] 5 years old, and with whom a good beginning on the Violin had already been made....[1]

Evidently the child displayed the same precocious musical talent as his brothers; but he was to die aged seven, on 26 October 1743, when his father was away on campaign. Caroline records what she had later been told:

> About this time my Mother had the afflicting task laid on her to acquaint my Father with the loss of his second Son, of whom he was doatingly fond. He was 7 years and 6 months old when he died.[2]

Of the cause of his death we know nothing.

William

Friedrich Wilhelm (known to history as William, the name he took when he settled in England) was born on 15 November 1738, the fourth of Isaac and Anna's
children and their third son. Before he was three years old the War of the Austrian
Succession disrupted the Herschel family life, as Isaac's regiment marched out of
Hanover in the autumn of 1741. Although on this occasion they were back in a
matter of weeks, the scene was set for years of campaigning, and it was not until
February 1746, when William was seven years old, that Isaac was at last able to
return permanently to his family. Broken in health, he sought and was granted
'dismission' from the army.

William had followed his siblings into the Garrison School, but during 1747 his
education was interrupted by Isaac's ill-judged decision to move the family to the
vicinity of Hamburg. They returned to Hanover at the end of the year following an
informal bargain between Isaac and General Wangenheim, and Isaac rejoined the
band of the Guards, along with Jacob who was just fourteen. The general undertook that William would be auditioned for the band when he was of the necessary
age,[1] so we know that the music lessons Isaac had been giving him since he was
old enough to hold a small violin[2] were already bearing fruit. At school William's
abilities had led to the master's asking him "to hear younger boys say their lessons
and to examine their arithmetical calculations";[3] and Isaac paid for him to attend
the teacher's private classes in Latin and arithmetic.[4] After William was accepted
into the Guards band in May 1753 following an audition on the oboe and violin with
General Sommerfeld,[5] Isaac put some of his son's wages towards lessons in French.
Finding William an unusually apt and enquiring pupil, the teacher introduced him
to logic, ethics and metaphysics.[6]

Soon however Isaac's worst fears were realized as war-clouds began to gather
once more, and in March 1756 the Guards sailed to England as reinforcements
against a possible French invasion.[7] William took the opportunity to learn some
English,[8] and he made enough progress to justify the purchase of John Locke's classic
treatise, *An Essay Concerning Human Understanding*.[9] The two brothers also made
contacts among local musicians[10] that would one day stand them in good stead.

In the autumn of 1756 Jacob at last obtained the dismission he had been seeking
for some months, and returned home, followed in January[11] by Isaac and William
along with the regiment. But soon Hanover itself was threatened by the French.
On 1 May 1757 the Guards marched out of the town,[12] to take part in a campaign
in which the musicians had as usual to share the discomforts of the soldiers:

my Father and I went with the regiment into a campaign which proved very harassing, by many forced marches and bad accommodations. We were many times obliged, after a fatiguing day, to erect our tents in a ploughed field, the furrows of which were full of water.[13]

On 26 July the two armies met at the Battle of Hastenbeck. During the battle, if we are to believe what William told his son many years later, "with balls flying over his head he walked behind a hedge spouting speeches, rhetoric then being his favourite study".[14] The Hanoverians and their allies were defeated. Isaac was more concerned for William than himself, and "advised me to look to my own safety" and to go home to Hanover.[15] But there William found the town hastily organizing defences against the French who were expected any time, and any able-bodied young man risked "being pressed for a soldier".[16] In the regiment, musicians were at least recognized as non-combatants: William was out of the frying pan and into the fire. He therefore decided to rejoin his father. Borrowing a greatcoat from their landlord, he slipped out of town, followed at a discreet distance by his mother who carried a bundle with his accoutrements. Once clear of the sentries, he changed into uniform, and bade Anna farewell.[17]

Not surprisingly, in the chaos his absence had not been noticed.[18] But Isaac was far from happy at the reappearance of his son, and there followed weeks during which "The weather was uncommonly hot and the continual marches were very harassing".[19] Isaac thereupon decided on another plan: William was too young to have taken the oath and so (in his father's opinion) was entitled to quit the field of battle, and to head for Hamburg *en route* for the safety of England. There, as a musician with local contacts, he could surely find work.[20] Caroline portrays the next skirmish as settling the matter,

> for when hearing the balls whistle over their heads through the branches of the tree under which they had taken shelter, my Father cried out Go! Go! waving his hand towards Hamburg Go! you have no business here.[21]

William, seeing that "no body seemed to mind whether the Musicians were present or absent",[22] gladly took his father's advice. Somehow Isaac got word to Jacob, a civilian but in danger of being pressed into the defence of Hanover, that he should do likewise. The brothers duly met up in Hamburg around the end of October, and it was not long before they reached England.[23]

1757–1766: THE ITINERANT REFUGEE

Isaac had been able to find the money his sons would need for their passage to England only by borrowing from a family to whom he was music teacher,[24] and this had stretched his credit to the limit. The result was that when Jacob and William arrived in London in November they were almost destitute. William later told his son John that he did not have half a guinea in his pocket,[25] and so he went into a music shop and offered to copy music. He was given an opera to write out, and so pleased was the shopkeeper with the results that William was able to earn a modest living in this way until something better turned up.[26]

Fortunately the contacts they had made with English musicians during their previous visit stood them in good stead, and before long Jacob had pupils to teach. The following summer "we visited some families in and near Maidstone and Rochester, and had a concert at Tunbridge Wells".[27]

London, however, was "overstocked with musicians", and the brothers were no more than young men newly arrived from abroad and barely on the thresholds of their careers. A further complication was that Jacob, the elder and musically the more talented, had a high opinion of his own abilities, and refused to play second fiddle under any circumstances. To save the two of them from starvation, therefore, William had little choice but to copy music and teach such pupils as he could attract. In this way they struggled on as best they could, until the late summer of 1759, when the Hanoverian forces and their allies defeated the French at the Battle of Minden and expelled them from the region. That September Jacob was offered his long-sought-after place in the Court Orchestra at Hanover. He departed for home, leaving William (according to Caroline) to pay his tailor's bills "and parting with his last farthing for traveling expenses".[28] Even the long-suffering William records that "Having given everything I could possibly spare to my brother when he left me I found myself involved in great difficulties".[29]

Jacob was a civilian and there was no obstacle to his return to Hanover. William's status is less clear. He had quit his regiment, not as a peace-time deserter, but in the chaotic aftermath of battle. Moreover, he was a boy and not under oath. Isaac's view had been that William was therefore fully entitled to go. Yet Caroline tells us that Isaac "was put in Arest by way of enforcing the return of the Deserter",[30] which shows that the authorities took a very different view. Certainly William had received no formal discharge; and were he to have returned with Jacob to rejoin their family in Hanover, he would have had to resume his place in a military service of which he had bitter memories, and in a post unworthy of his abilities.

That he himself saw his current status as less than creditable is confirmed by the autobiographical letter he wrote in 1784 in response to an invitation from Charles Hutton, editor of the *Ladies Diary*. William tells Hutton that he practised music in Hanover until wartime troubles "made my situation there very uncomfortable. The known encouragem^t given to Music in England determined me to try my fortune abroad & accordingly ab^t the year 1759 I came to settle in this country ...".[31] The most charitable verdict on this version of events is that William was being economical with the truth.

Whether it was open to him to pay even a brief visit to his family is doubtful. Although from time to time in letters to Jacob he makes remarks such as "I will try and make a visit to Hanover",[32] the proposal in his letter of 13 March 1762 has an important qualification: he talks of travelling to Hanover next winter "to see my relations, (if I get my discharge by your means)".[33] In fact the discharge was issued on 29 March by General A. F. v. Spörcken,[34] so it would seem that Jacob used his influence in Court circles to good and rapid effect — and that then and only then was it open to William to visit Hanover.

With Jacob gone, London overstocked with musicians, and his own bitter memories of the Hanoverian Guards, William turned his thoughts to the English provinces. "Very opportunely I had an offer of going into Yorkshire where the Earl of Darlington wanted a good Musician to be at the head of a small band for a regiment of militia of which he was the General."[35] The band was small indeed: two oboists and two (talented) French horns; but William was to be paid his travelling expenses and the engagement could be terminated on a month's notice, and so he gladly accepted.[36] William records that he went to Yorkshire by coach, but Caroline reports that he told her he went on foot and pocketed the expenses.[37]

Such appointments were not of course full-time. Rather, they provided a steady job with a basic income that could be supplemented by free-lance teaching and performing. Such an arrangement provided a lifestyle that greatly appealed to William's temperament. He was a hardworking young man who hated to be idle — "My love for activity makes it absolutely necessary that I should be busy, for I grow sick by idleness, — it kills me almost to do nothing";[38] but he felt the need for the security of an assured even if modest salary.[39]

Lord Darlington's offer therefore suited him well; and for the next eighteen months William trained his little band and wrote suitable music for them, while in his spare time he undertook musical engagements in towns and aristocratic homes in different parts of Yorkshire. In the intervals between engagements he composed symphonies and concertos, for it was then his ambition to be remembered as a composer.[40] Soon he found himself able to make time for private study. After his English had reached an acceptable standard he began to learn Italian because of its importance to singers, and he then revived the Latin he had learned from his schoolmaster. Greek proved a step too far.[41] Instead, he developed his interest in the mathematics underlying musical harmony, and this led him on to the study of 'fluxions' and other branches of mathematics.[42]

William later had to reconstruct his movements in this period from the places and dates written at the head of his musical scores and from his letters to Jacob. In each of the years 1760, 1761 and 1762 he composed six symphonies;[43] and early in 1761 he began to write Jacob a succession of letters, consecutively paginated, that were for the most part mini-treatises dealing with a variety of themes including music. It is difficult for the historian to work up much enthusiasm for these somewhat priggish and pretentious effusions, though a remark in a letter of October 1761 hints at an awakening interest in the universe around him: "If one observes the whole natural world as one, one finds everything in the most beautiful order; it is my favourite maxim: 'Tout est dans l'ordre.'"[44]

It is in his letter of 4 February 1761 that he tells Jacob of an impending visit to Edinburgh. Evidently he had heard that the manager of the concerts there was about to leave, and he hoped to be appointed in his stead. Such a post would be more worthy of his talents than the little quartet of the Darlington Militia.

At Edinburgh, William was invited to lead the band in a performance that included some of his symphonies and concertos, and he dined with the meta-physician David Hume. The guests formed "a considerable company, all of whom were pleased to express their approbation of my musical talents",[45] and William returned to Yorkshire confident that the post was his. He therefore resigned from the Militia — after all, even if his appointment was not confirmed, his freelance work in Yorkshire was now enough to guarantee him a living.

Unfortunately, the Edinburgh manager withdrew his resignation and decided to stay, and so William found himself a purely itinerant musician; it was only then, it seems, that he realized how important to him were security and stability. It was not that he was pressed for cash — he estimated he was earning three times Jacob's salary from the Court Orchestra[46] — but the loneliness and uncertainty of life as a freelance did not suit his temperament. He took refuge in composing symphonies, and in adding to the pile of mini-treatises addressed to Jacob (over seventy pages on Locke's book alone[47]), but he became depressed. To Jacob he confided: "But I must tell you a certain anxiety attends a vagrant life. I do daily meet with vexations and trouble and live only by hope."[48]

The constant journeying on horseback was one source of aggravation and even danger:

> ... I will only say that at 9 o'clock, when I had still about 20 miles to ride, I was caught in an unusually heavy thunderstorm, which continued accompanied by torrents of rain, with unbroken fury, for three hours, and threatened me with sudden death. The distance from an habitation, the darkness and loneli-ness, obliged me nevertheless to ride on. I pursued my way therefore with unshaken sangfroid although I was often obliged to shut my eyes on account of the blinding lightening. At last the flashes all around me were so terrifying that my horse refused to go on; luckily at this moment I found myself near a house, into which, after much knocking, I was admitted. This morning, at 3 o'clock, I proceeded on my journey and arrived safely at this place.[49]

In August 1761 there was an encouraging development: he was summoned by his friends Sir Ralph and Lady Milbank, and found himself spending a week making music with the Duke of York.[50] "Whether this acquaintance with the Duke will be of any advantage to me I cannot yet say."[51] That same month he took charge of a band of sixteen players in a weekly concert in Newcastle, held in a garden after the style of Vauxhall in London. He had all the money he needed for his modest life-style, but "All the same I live as a hermit. No one troubles about me and I trouble about very few".[52]

By the following January he was finding the itinerant life so depressing that he considered giving up music altogether:

I do not know what will become of me at last; my present way of living will not do, and I must soon change or I shall never get forward. I am as it were buried here, and tho' I do not want for anything, yet I am very far from being satisfied with my way of life.... I have for some time been thinking of leaving off professing music, and the first opportunity that offers, I shall really do so....[53]

Two months later he was actively searching for a stable position: "I am at present looking about for some sort or other of a place, either as organist or any other of a fixed kind, which it is not at all unlikely I may find, as I have the good luck to make friends everywhere."[54]

Within weeks his prayers were answered. On 16 April 1762, at a concert in Leeds, he played two solos, "and though these were much praised, I got more pleasure from finding that my symphony had such a success that I was heartily congratulated on being the composer".[55] Five days later there was a concert with a singer from York who brought with him a colleague to play first violin. The Leeds directors wished William to lead the orchestra, but he thought it better to let the visitor have first place. However, rather than be second fiddle, William played the accompaniment on the clavecin. In the second part of the concert the violinist played a solo, at which the audience insisted that William do the same, in a trial of their competing abilities. Afterwards the other violinist graciously conceded defeat, while "Some went so far as to say I was the best violinist they had ever heard".[56]

Another successful concert quickly followed, after which William could report to Jacob:

Some of the leading and richest people in this town have interested themselves so much in me that there is talk of retaining me here; and if their intention succeeds (as I greatly hope) this town will put a pleasant end to my restless weary life.

They talk of giving me a salary of perhaps even 4 of 5 hundred thalers, but rather than leave this delightful place, I would be content to begin with 2 hundred thalers, as I am sure in a couple of years I could make it up to 600, and besides I should have a beautiful opportunity here to become known as a composer, which is always my chief ambition.[57]

William was duly appointed director of the public concerts at Leeds. He lodged with a Mr and Mrs Bulman, and this proved so satisfactory that he would later arrange for them to follow him to Bath.

William was to spend over four years at Leeds, in the middle of which he received his discharge from the Hanoverian Guards and so could at last visit his family in Hanover and reassure his ailing father about his prospects in England.[58] The period is thinly represented in his "Memorandums", but his letters to Jacob betray occasional anxiety as to whether he will be continued in the Leeds post. On 13 February 1763 he tells his brother, "If I could only be sure that I could keep my present place for certain, I might give you an invitation to come over for a couple of years".[59] Two months later he is more confident: "... as everything has gone very successfully [in the concerts] I shall probably remain here some years."[60] Perhaps it was this element of uncertainty that kept him open to alternative offers of employment. In March 1766 we find him in Halifax, some 14 miles from Leeds, rehearsing *Messiah* with a private club of chorus singers who intended to perform the oratorio in the church when a new organ by the great Johann Snetzler was installed. William decided to compete for the post of organist,[61] payment for which was to be a guinea per Sunday,[62] and he persuaded the organist at Leeds to let him practise there in preparation for the competition, which was to be held on 30 August.[63] Meanwhile he deputized at both Leeds and Wakefield when the regular organists were on holiday.

1766–1782: MUSIC AND ASTRONOMY IN BATH

On 9 August 1766, before the competition took place, William received a letter from Bath in the west of England.[64] It was written by Mrs Julia De Chair, wife of one of the two proprietors of a private chapel then being built in the fashionable spa resort.[65] The four parish churches in Bath were no longer able to cope with the numbers who wished to attend, and the Octagon Chapel in Milsom Street, the third of its kind, would allow members of its aristocratic congregation to worship their Maker in warmth and comfort on payment of the appropriate rent. (The Octagon survives to this day, although it has long since ceased to be a chapel.) Mrs De Chair evidently told William that the chapel was to have an organ and asked if he would be a candidate for the post of organist. He must have sent an encouraging reply, for three weeks later Mrs De Chair wrote again, to confirm that he had been nominated.[66]

The very day after this letter reached him, William won the Halifax competition from a field of seven candidates.[67] It was three more days before he replied to Mrs De Chair.[68] In his autobiographical memoranda he does not specify the contents of his letter, but it is likely that he provisionally accepted, subject perhaps to improved terms. He heard from Mrs De Chair again on 9 October, and the next day he wrote confirming his acceptance. At Bath there was a vibrant musical life, which would offer many opportunities for him to supplement his income as organist: membership, and perhaps one day directorship, of the band that entertained the aristocratic visitors during the winter season (and Dr De Chair was a member of the concert committee[69]); the possibility of promoting private-enterprise 'benefit concerts' in his own right; performances in the private homes of the gentry; and, of course, the teaching that he so much enjoyed. On 18 October he gave notice of resignation as organist at Halifax, to take effect at the end of the quarter, and he was not dissuaded when a friend "communicated to me a proposal from the Gentlemen at Hallifax to increase my Salary if it would induce me to stay".[70]

William arrived in Bath on 9 December, and took rooms with the Harper family in

The Octagon Chapel, courtesy of the William Herschel Museum.

Bell Lane. Soon he found himself enchanted by their daughter Elizabeth. Elizabeth sang as she sewed, and in no time William was giving her lessons; however, "on disclosing his passion he received no encouragement".[71]

Snetzler would not have the chapel organ ready for months, and meanwhile William had the opportunity to establish himself on the musical scene. On New Year's Day he hired the Assembly Room for a benefit concert in which he played his own compositions on no fewer than three different instruments: violin, oboe, and harpsichord.[72] Not surprisingly there was a thin attendance to hear the unknown artist, but afterwards word went round that a new talent had arrived. On 23 January William was invited by the Master of Ceremonies to join the band.[73] The band was funded out of the visitors' subscriptions in the Assembly Room, Pump Room, and Baths;[74] and to be a member of the band guaranteed a regular income.

The occasions could be quite splendid. A participant in a performance held in December 1779 wrote:

> ... found the most brilliant Assembly my Eyes ever beheld. The Elegance of the room, illuminated with 480 wax Candles, the prismatic colours of the Lustres, the blaze of Jewels, and the inconceivable Harmony of near 40 Musicians, some of whom are the finest hands on Europe, added to the rich attire of about 800 Gentlemen and Ladies, was, altogether, a scene of which no

person who never saw it can form any adequate Idea — It began at half past 6 and ended at 10.[75]

Nevertheless William refused the invitation to play second fiddle, until he learned that the band included no less a person than Thomas Linley, Sr, who with his large and talented family dominated musical life in Bath; and that, like Linley, he would be privileged to send a deputy when it was not convenient to play in person — that is, when a more lucrative engagement offered. At this he accepted.[76]

Early in the new year William had advertised in a local paper offering lessons on the guitar, harpsichord, violin and singing, to be given at his lodgings with Mr Harper;[77] and he may also have taught the oboe and cello.[78] Before long the number of William's pupils had grown to the point where he needed to rent a house for himself. Remembering the successful arrangement he had enjoyed for so long with the Bulmans in Leeds, and knowing that Mr Bulman's business there had since failed and that his friend was in financial difficulties, William saw a way to solve two problems at a single stroke: he used his influence at the Octagon Chapel to secure Mr Bulman the post of Clerk, and he invited the family to join him in his new home where Mrs Bulman would run the establishment as before. By April they were together once more, installed in a house in Beauford Square.[79]

Meanwhile work progressed on the chapel and its organ.[80] The ambitious proprietors hoped that the liturgy there might imitate that of a cathedral, and William's duties would be by no means confined to playing the organ at services. He was to train a choir and write suitably simple music for them to perform.[81] In June, installation of the organ began,[82] and on the 24th, Jacob, drawn like a bee to financial honey, arrived on an extended visit. In July William hired soloists for the performances of Handel's *Messiah* that were to provide the opening celebrations.[83] For his choir, if we are to believe a German periodical, he enlisted "young workmen, carpenters and joiners, who had no previous notion of singing, but who, under his stimulating tuition, were soon able to render the choruses of various oratorios with success".[84]

On 18 October and again the following day there were performances of *Messiah*, the proceeds going to "the relief of the industrious poor". William led the orchestra, while Jacob played the organ. William himself performed an organ concerto between the second and third parts, and as if all this was not enough, he arranged a benefit concert on his own account to take place later on the first of the two evenings.[85]

Bath was a place of limitless opportunities for musicians of talent and energy, and William's activities increased and multiplied in the years that followed. He was much sought-after as a teacher, and in a single week he might give an hour's lesson to as many as forty-six pupils,[86] some of them from the aristocracy and no doubt generous with their payments.[87] He arranged series of private concerts in stately homes where his pupils would perform, accompanied by a small group of professionals. In the winter of 1775/6, for example,

By the arrangement of the Marchioness of Lothian, her own private concerts and those that occasionally were given by Ladies of her part were modelled into a regular succession so that one of them was to be held every Saturday evening at the house of one of the Ladies who joined the party. As the music was chiefly to con[s]ist of the singing and Harpsichord playing of my Scholars I engaged only a sufficient accompanyment to make up a quartetto. Twenty of these concerts were given on so many successive Saturdays. They began Novr 11, 1775 and ended the 27th of March 1776. Among those who attended were Lady Malpas, Lady Deans, Marchioness of Lothian, Duchess of Marlborough, Duchess of Ancaster, Lady Dorothy Ingles, The Dean of Ossory, Mrs Crespigny, Mrs Dechair &c.[88]

And all this was in addition to his duties at the chapel and with the town band.

For a Bath musician, life was highly seasonal: a non-stop round of engagements from autumn to Easter was followed by summer months when the visitors were gone and the town quiet. William had no difficulty in securing summer work out of town: "1767 May 10 & 11. A visit to Belmont the Seat of the Marchioness of Clanricarde. I went on Horseback by Salisbury, Winchester, Belmont ab[ou]t 72 miles. I stayed there two days and the third I returned to Bath. I attended Lady Amelia and Lady [Augusta] Dubourgh in this manner once a fortnight during the Summer season."[89] He also involved himself in the customary if limited summer entertainments in Bath; at Spring Gardens, for example, informal "cotillons and country dances" were traditionally performed to the accompaniment of horns and clarinets, and William wrote madrigals, catches and glees. In June 1768 the *Bath Chronicle* announced:

> The Musical Evening Entertainment at Spring Gardens under the conduct of Mr Herschel will be continued Wednesdays and Saturdays during the Summer Season.— To consist of Vocal and Instrumental MUSIC divided into THREE ACTS, and to begin at Six o'clock precisely.— 1/- entrance – Tea, Coffee, If wet music in the Rooms.[90]

The following year William notes in his Memorandums, "In the Summer I attended Plays at Bristol"; and such was his success as a teacher that in October he published as "Lessons for Scholars" six sonatas for harpsichord with optional violin and cello.[91] Astonishingly, he later embarked on a "Spiritual Opera" based on Milton's *Paradise Lost*, a chorus from which was performed at Bath in 1780, and he wrote a number of pieces for "an intended Tragic Comic Opera ... the Desert Island"; but neither work progressed very far. With all this activity it is no wonder that not long after his arrival, he was earning more from music than the Astronomer Royal from astronomy.[92]

But such opportunities made Bath a cockpit of rivalries: benefit concerts could be lucrative if there were no competing functions the same day and if the most fashionable performers took part; if not, they could be expensive failures. These

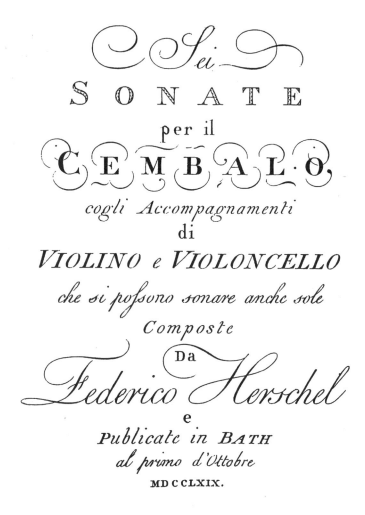

The title-page of the six harpsichord lessons in the form of sonatas with optional violin and cello accompaniment, published by William in 1769. In his own list of his compositions (See ref. 91) he explains: "My two christian names being Frederick William, the first of them (Federico in italian) is only put to the publication."

rivalries were exacerbated in 1771 when the New Assembly Rooms (which survive to this day) were opened in direct competition with the Old. William may have hoped to be appointed director of music there, but Linley was the one chosen and William was assigned only a marginal function, as one of the extra musicians for the Wednesday concerts. Tensions mounted between the two men, and soon their squabble was being conducted in the newspapers. William's absurd pretext for the confrontation, announced in an advertisement in the *Bath Chronicle* for 9 January 1772, was the "ungenteel treatment" he had suffered through Linley's failure to provide him with a music stand for two nights running, forcing him "on Account of that Deficiency, to place his Books upon the Ground".

That the equable William should resort to public abuse is testimony to how high passions could run among Bath musicians, and to how far the opening of the New Rooms had upset the established order. Linley, tongue in cheek, replied sympathizing with the "grievous wound" William had received, which "must violently agitate the tender Sensibility of his Frame". William retorted that the "sensibility of Mr. Linley's *Frame*" was evidently not "tender enough to perceive the real Offence there is in leaving *any* Gentleman of the Band two *successive* Nights without a Desk". Before long Linley was characterizing William as a man of "mean and contemptible Disposition"; Linley was glad to inform him of "how very sincerely he despised him", comments that William ascribed to "that bitterness of Temper which is the general Attendant on low Cunning and dark Envy, when they are drawn out of their lurking Place and exposed to Public View".[93]

The Old Rooms retained their loyal following, and were more conveniently located for the less mobile, and so William transferred his allegiance there and mounted a rival series of concerts.[94] He also enlarged his private musical practice.

It was during this winter of 1771/2 that William began to plan the rescue from Hanover of his younger sister Caroline, who was then languishing in the family home, a household drudge with no evident means of escape. William was well informed about the plight of his little sister: their brother Alexander had settled in Bath and was living with William and the Bulmans. He it was who suggested to William the possibility that Caroline might make a career as a singer, if only she could escape from Hanover and join them in Bath.

Caroline was thrilled, but soon Jacob — the head of the household following the death of their father — turned against the proposal. However, it chanced that Jacob was absent with the Court Orchestra when William arrived in Hanover in August 1772, to take his sister to Bath if she so wished. The outcome was inevitable: Caroline put her fate into William's hands.[95]

Among William's brief memoranda for his early years in Bath there is no mention whatever of astronomy, but by the time he collected Caroline from Hanover he was beginning to develop a passion for the subject. She records that as they drove across Holland by coach William introduced her to the constellations, and on their stopover in London on their way to Bath, the shops to which she was invited to accompany him were those of opticians.[96]

Back in 1766, when he was still in Yorkshire, William had recorded in his memoranda[97] that "My leisure time was employed in reading mathematical Books such as the works of Emerson,[98] Maclaurin,[99] Hodgson,[100] Dr Smith's Harmonics &c".[101] In a letter to Charles Hutton written in 1784, William clarifies the sequence of events. As a musician in Hanover he had studied the mathematical theory of harmony, and this led him when settled in England to acquire a copy of Robert Smith's

Harmonics, so triggering a chain of events "by which means I was drawn on from one branch of the Mathematics to another".[102] Smith had until 1760 been Plumian Professor of Astronomy at Cambridge, and it must have been William's satisfaction with *Harmonics* that led him at some stage (perhaps 1771 or early 1772) to buy the two substantial quarto volumes of Smith's *A Compleat System of Opticks*.[103] There he found comprehensive accounts of the theory of optics and of methods for the construction of telescopes and microscopes, beginning with the grinding and polishing and ending with techniques for using the completed instruments. William rarely if ever had occasion to visit London, and the day he spent there with Caroline gave him the chance to see optical instruments that previously he had (in all probability) known only through the printed pages of Smith's treatise.

Rarely if ever in the history of astronomy has the purchase of a book had such momentous consequences. William had briefly flirted with astronomical observations during his last year in Leeds, for amid brief notes of musical engagements, he records: "Feb 19. Wheatley. Observation of Venus", and "[Feb] 24 Eclipse of the moon at 7 o'clock A.M."[104] Now his interest in the various branches of mathematics had led him to optics, and he held in his hands a book that opened up great possibilities. He would one day tell Hutton that "with the assistance of the directions given in Dr Smith's optics" he was sure he could make himself a reflecting telescope that otherwise would be beyond his purse; indeed, he noted in 1776 that "with the assistance of my mathematical knowledge, the optics of Dr Smith and mechanics of Emerson, I found no difficulties but what I could get the better of".[105] And not only that, but Smith's Book IV also provided a "history of telescopical discoveries in the heavens". Brief though the Book was, William could now look on telescopes as the means and the exploration of the heavens as the end.

But for the present there was little time for astronomy, for Caroline's arrival in Bath on 27 August 1772 was soon followed by the opening of the winter season. For her part she accepted that William would be preoccupied in the weeks ahead and unable to spare time for her. But when the season drew to a close around Easter, she felt entitled to more of his time.[106]

She was disappointed. William's brief autobiographical memoranda, hitherto almost exclusively devoted to listing concerts and music lessons, suddenly switch to astronomy:

> 1773 Aprl 19. Bought a Quadrant[107] and Emerson's Trigonometry.[108]
> May 1. Sigra Farinelli's Concert.
> 10. Bought a book of Astronomy,[109] and one of astronomical tables.
> 24. Bought an object glass of 10 feet focal length.
> June 1. Bought many eyeglasses, and tin tubes made. A pair of steps.
> 7. Glasses paid for and the use of a small reflector paid for....[110]

The principle on which a Hadley's quadrant operated was similar to that of the nautical sextant, but it had a 90° scale engraved on an arc of 45°. We note that William bought the quadrant three weeks before he invested in "a book of Astronomy" — James Ferguson's *Astronomy Explained upon Sir Isaac Newton's Principles* — and so there is no doubt that Smith's Book IV (rather than Ferguson's *Astronomy*) played the crucial role in attracting him to astronomy. What then would he have learned from Smith's brief treatise?

Smith's chapters on the Sun, Moon and planets — then the preoccupation of all professionals and most amateurs — were unremarkable. But in the final chapter, "Telescopical discoveries in the Fixt Stars", William encountered some of the issues that were to form his life's work in the science. Smith described the number of stars revealed by the telescope, "the more of them as the aperture is more enlarged to take in more light";[111] later, William's unrelenting quest for "more light" would culminate in his construction of a monster reflector with mirrors 4-ft in diameter, the like of which the world had never seen. Smith reported Bradley's conclusion that the nearest stars were at least 400,000 times as far as the Sun, though just how far away they were no one knew;[112] William, as we shall see, would collect hundreds of 'double stars' in an attempt to contribute to this problem. Smith reported three examples of "new stars", striking changes among the *stellae fixae* of Antiquity; at the end of the century William was to publish long catalogues of sequences of stars in order of brightness, in the expectation that a variable would disturb a sequence and thus betray its presence. Most important of all, Smith mentioned the mysterious "lucid spots" observed in Orion, Andromeda and elsewhere;[113] William, and indeed Caroline and William's son John, were each to dedicate a major part of their lives to the collection and examination of nebulae in the hope of elucidating this mystery.

As befitted a book dedicated to astronomy, Ferguson's *Astronomy* provided William with a more extended account of such "discoveries". Ferguson had begun life as a shepherd-boy, and his schooling lasted just three months. But he developed into an ingenious constructor of models of celestial movements, and this caught the attention of Professor Colin Maclaurin of Edinburgh. Eventually Ferguson became unofficial popularizer-in-residence to the Court, the recipient of a 'pension' from the King of £50 a year, and a Fellow of the Royal Society.[114]

Ferguson's *Astronomy* was a popular best-seller, first published in 1756 and still appearing in new editions in the early nineteenth century. The 1756 edition dealt with the solar system together with the tides, the equation of time, the calculation of new and full moons and eclipses, and Ferguson's own mechanical models. But his approach to astronomy was not that of a professional, for he lost no opportunity to insist that the whole universe was populated with intelligent beings; William, by doing likewise in research papers intended for publication, was to have a troubled entry into Royal Society circles.

In his opening pages Ferguson declares that "all the Planets and Moons, in the [Solar] System, are designed as commodious habitations for creatures endowed with capacities of knowing and adoring their beneficent Creator". Indeed, "From what we know of our own System, it may reasonably be concluded that all the rest are with equal wisdom contrived, situated, and provided with accommodations for rational inhabitants".[115] He later devotes four paragraphs to exploring what life is like for the inhabitants of the Moon. For example:

> 60. There being no Atmosphere about the Moon, the heavens in the day-time have the appearance of night to a Lunarian who turns his back toward the Sun; and when he does, the Stars appear as bright to him as they do in the night to us. For, it is entirely owing to our Atmosphere that the Heavens are bright about us in the day.

This then was the approach to astronomy that William absorbed as he read Ferguson in bed before falling asleep.

It is symptomatic of the current lack of interest in the stars that only in the second edition of 1757 did Ferguson add a chapter "Of the fixed Stars". Even so, it was a mere dozen pages in a volume of over five hundred. Nevertheless, as we read these pages with the benefit of hindsight, we find, time and again, the briefest of mentions of topics to which William would one day dedicate his immense energies.

The nearest stars (Ferguson avers without proof) are 32 million million miles away, and each is probably the centre of a planetary system; this "doctrine of the plurality of worlds is rational, and greatly manifests the Power, Wisdom, and Goodness of the Great Creator". After a routine account of the constellations, Ferguson briefly describes the Milky Way, "which is owing to a vast number of very small stars". He next lists a handful of "little whitish spots in the Heavens, which appear magnified, and more luminous when seen through telescopes; yet without any stars in them": these "lucid spots", as the marginal rubric calls them, include the nebula in Andromeda, which "is liable to several changes, and is sometimes invisible" (a misconception that had originated in the seventeenth century[116]). In addition there are "Cloudy, or nebulous Stars", which "look like dim Stars to the naked eye; but through a telescope they appear broad illuminated parts of the Sky". The most remarkable is in Orion's Sword, "where seven Stars, of which three are very close together, seem to shine through a cloud, very lucid near the middle, but faint and ill-defined about the edges. It looks like a gap in the sky, through which one may see (as it were) part of a much brighter region". Such nebulous stars are spaces "in which there seems to be a perpetual uninterrupted day among numberless Worlds, which no human art ever can discover". But, William evidently asked himself, was that pessimistic verdict warranted?

Perhaps the single most significant point made by Ferguson is summed up under the rubric, "The world not eternal". Newton and Leibniz had agreed that God is the great Clockmaker and that the universe is his masterpiece, and therefore its cyclic motions will continue indefinitely into the future. Ferguson believes to the contrary that the Moon moves in a resisting medium and therefore slows down and will one day fall to Earth, and that the planets similarly will in time collapse into the Sun.

Here we have a strong philosophical argument against the eternity of the World.... But we may be certain, that it will last as long as was intended by its Author, who ought no more to be found fault with for framing so perishable a work, than for making man mortal.

Ferguson, in short, sees gravity as an agent for change and eventual destruction, a concept that William was to make the foundation for his most creative ventures in astronomical theorizing.

Naturally William was eager to see these things for himself, and in the early summer of 1773 he began to assemble simple refracting telescopes. In the late seventeenth century the need to minimize chromatic aberration, which results from differences in the angles through which the colours that make up starlight are bent as they pass through the objective lens of a refractor, had led Christiaan Huygens and others to contrive telescopes of unmanageable lengths, and before long William found himself trying to view through a 30-ft refractor.

It was a revelation to experience the convenience of even a "small reflector", for in reflectors the light of every colour is equally reflected off a mirror. He told Hutton in his 1784 letter that the 2-ft reflector of Gregorian construction that he hired, "this being the best instrument the town would afford", was so satisfactory that this "determined me to furnish myself with a capital telesc[ope] & ignorant of the value of these instruments I desired a 5 f^t reflect^r to be made for me". The price he was quoted "tho' moderate appeared to me so extravagant that I formed the resolution to make myself one", with the aid of Smith's *Opticks*.[117]

Like many amateur astronomers before and since, William was confident he could teach himself to grind and polish mirrors for reflectors; but the problem was, how to get started. The solution came on Sunday 22 September 1773. After evening service in the Octagon Chapel, Caroline went straight home as usual; but William kept an appointment with a Quaker whose attempts to polish mirrors had met with little success, and who now wished to dispose of his bits and pieces.[118] These William bought, and soon he was launched on his career as one of the great telescope makers of all time.

Caroline was dismayed by all the activity:

> ... to my sorrow I saw almost every room turned into a workshop. A cabinet maker making a tube and stands of all descriptions in a handsome furnished drawing-room. Alex putting up a huge turning machine ... in a bedroom for turning patterns, grinding glasses and turning eye-pieces &c.[119]

The pattern of William's life for the years immediately ahead was now set. In the winter months he was a professional musician busy all hours; in the summer, with the willing help of Alexander and the less-willing help of Caroline, he was a telescope maker (and occasional observer).

From time to time during the winter season he would direct concerts in Bath or nearby Bristol (and occasionally elsewhere[120]), but on these we are poorly informed, because he tended to avoid incurring the expense of advertising, and the perform-ances were seldom reviewed. Teaching and the lucrative private concerts in the homes of the aristocracy probably provided the bulk of his income. But he took a leading role in the Handel oratorios that were customary during Lent, and which marked the culmination of the season.

In the spring of 1774, at the close of her second season, Caroline's hopes of sing-ing lessons from her brother were again disappointed, as she found herself swept up in the flurry of telescope making.[121] Astronomy was beginning to gain the upper hand in the competition between William's vocations of music and astronomy. On 1 March he had opened his first journal of observations. Like so many amateurs before and since, he first observed Saturn, and the planet's satellites and ring fascinated him: over the next month and a half he made observations on fourteen nights, and on twelve of these he examined Saturn. But, more significantly, the other object he observed on 1 March was the Orion Nebula, and on 4 March (see p. 136) he sketched its appearance:

> Saw the lucid Spot in Orions Sword, thro' a 5½ foot Reflector; its Shape was not as Dr Smith has delineated in his Optics; tho' something resembling it ... from this we may infer that there are undoubtedly changes among the fixt Stars, and perhaps from a careful observation of this Spot something might be concluded concerning the Nature of it.

Here, at the very outset of William's career as an observer, we find a succinct appraisal of the problem of the nature of the nebulae, an issue that was to divide astronomers well into the twentieth century. Obviously, a star cluster so distant that the individual stars could not be distinguished would appear milky, or 'nebulous'; but were all nebulae distant star clusters, or were some of them nearby clouds of luminous fluid or whatever?

If a nebula changed shape in only a few years (or even decades) it must be a nearby cloud, for very distant stars would appear virtually motionless over such a short span of time. William seems to have seized on this important test, here at the very start of his life as an astronomer. Having as yet no appreciation of how the appearance of a nebula can be affected by seeing conditions, the particular instrument in use, the acuity of the observer, and so on, he suspected that the Orion Nebula had changed since the date of Smith's sketch (which in fact had been made by Christiaan Huygens in 1656[122]). If so it could not be a vast and distant star cluster. This was the beginning of his epoch-making researches into 'the construc-tion of the heavens'.

After the flurry of observations of Saturn in March and April 1774, William once more concentrated his work in astronomy on telescope-building. The Bul-mans returned to Leeds,[123] and at midsummer the Herschels moved from 7 New King Street, where William had resided since June 1769, to a house near Walcot Parade,[124] where they were to live for five years. Although "a little way out of town" and therefore inconveniently distant from the centres of musical life, the house "afforded more room for workshops and a place on the roof for observing".[125] Not only that, but the landlord was a builder who lived next door, and William could enlist his workmen to help when required. Two years later his construction efforts came to fruition: in May 1776 he completed, first a reflector of 7-ft focal length, and then a 10-ft. On 28 May he spent some three hours studying the Moon with the 10-ft reflector, and then devoted three folio pages to an account of what he had seen:

> ... I believed to perceive something which I immediately took to be <u>growing Substances</u>, I will not call them Trees as from their size they can hardly come under that denomination.... My attention was chiefly directed to Mare humorum, and this I now believe to be a <u>forest</u>, this word being also taken in its proper extended signification as consisting of such large <u>growing Substances</u>. In the annexed figure ... there is a <u>Wood</u> which goes up to mount Gassendus.[126]

A couple of months later he resumed his reflections on the analogy between the Earth and the Moon. "Do not all the Elements seem at war here, when we compare the Earth with the moon. Air, Water, Fire, Clouds, tempests, Vulcanos &c: all these are either not on the Moon, or at least kept i[n] much greater subjection than here." His verdict: "For my part, were I to chuse between the Moon & earth I should not hesitate a moment to fix upon the Moon for my Habitation."[127]

How are we to detect proof of life on the Moon? Our new towns, canals and main roads will be visible from the Moon, and we for our part should look out for similar structures on the Moon. "But this is no easy undertaking to make out, and will require the Observation of many a careful Astronomer, and the most capital Instruments that can be had. However this is what I will begin."[128] Fortunately, he soon abandoned this bizarre enterprise, and concentrated instead on measuring the heights of the lunar mountains.

In July 1776 he erected his first major telescope, a 20-ft reflector slung from a pole, with mirrors 12 inches in diameter.[129] These mirrors were of a high quality, the eyepieces even more remarkable than William realized — all it lacked was a stable mounting. It was a promising start.

Meanwhile he had to earn his living. In 1776 the two men who had established the Octagon Chapel parted company. De Chair's associate, William Street, took sole control, and appointed a new minister and a new organist.[130] Whether this was by agreement with William we do not know, since neither he nor Caroline has left us any comment. Certainly the split came at a most convenient time, for Linley had recently departed Bath for London, and William took his place as Director of the New Assembly Rooms band.[131] But the tension between William's competing vocations took its toll. He was perfectly capable of mounting the most successful performances when his mind was on the job; but his concerts were not a success, and a year later Linley was invited back.[132]

The actor John Bernard in his *Retrospections of the Stage* devotes six full pages to an affectionate portrait of William as he was seen in the musical and acting fraternity of Bath around this time. Bernard

> attended him twice a week [for singing lessons], at his own lodgings, which then resembled an astronomer's much more than a musician's, being heaped up with globes, maps, telescopes, reflectors, &c., under which his piano was hid, and the violoncello, like a discarded favourite, skulked away in a corner.[133]

On another occasion,

> having a difficult song, I went as usual to my clever friend to rehearse it. It was cold and clear weather, but the sky that night was rather cloudy, and the moon peeped out only now and then from her veil. Herschel had a fire in his back apartment, and placed the music stand near its window, which I could not account for. He then procured his violin, and commenced the song, playing over the air twice or thrice to familiarize me with its general idea; and then leading me note by note to its thorough acquaintance. We got through about five bars pretty well, till of a sudden the sky began to clear up, and his eye was unavoidably attracted by the celestial bodies coming out, as it were, one by one from their hiding places: my eye, however, was fixed on the book: and when he exclaimed "Beautiful! beautiful!" squinting up at the stars, I thought he alluded to the music. At length, the whole host [of stars] threw aside their drapery, and stood forth in naked loveliness:— the effect was sudden and subduing, — "Beautiful, beautiful," shouted Herschel, "there he is at last!" dropping the fiddle, snatching a telescope, throwing up the window, and (though it was a night in January) beginning to survey an absentee planet, which he had been looking for.[134]

Towards the end of his time in Bath, William notes that some of his pupils "made me give them astronomical in stead of musical lessons".[135] He was "called by the charitably disposed an eccentric".[136] Even those pupils who simply needed help with their music became the object of merriment. Bernard records:

> When it was known that I attended him privately, the actors swore that I was studying astronomy, which rendered me the butt of the Green-room, and fair game for every society I entered. I was gravely asked at table whether I "advocated Tycho Brahe, or Copernicus?" and what was my "opinion of Sir Isaac Newton's Treatise on Fluxions?" whilst others stopped me in the street to inquire if I "had calculated the period of the last comet's return."[137]

At rehearsals, William became notorious for his distraction from the business at hand, and his fellow performers would say "He's in the clouds again, he's star-gazing!".

> Nowhere more than at the theatre, in a long musical rehearsal, was he given to this celestial absorption of ideas, and nowhere so much was he exposed to sarcasm, both from the stage and the orchestra, whenever it was perceived.[138]

In the spring of 1777, Caroline sang as a principal in the Lenten oratorios, and it seemed that a career beckoned; but when the season ended, she found to her dismay that the Herschel household reverted once more to astronomy. On seven evenings in late March and April William observed Saturn, and other planets as well on four of those evenings.

On his return to Bath that autumn, Linley found himself facing intense competition from the rival concerts in the Old Rooms, whose managers had enlisted a talented young violinist named Franz Lamotte.[139] William, for his part, organized sixteen private events in aristocratic homes.[140] But at the turn of the year both Linley and Lamotte departed, and William found himself in charge of concerts at both Rooms and in nearby Bristol as well.[141]

Lamotte returned for the concerts held in the autumn of 1778, although William was in charge again in the spring of 1779.[142] In his Memorandums for that summer, William insists that, despite his involvement in the concerts in the Gardens, "All my leisure time was employed in grinding and polishing 7, 10 and 20 feet mirrors and making observations with them".[143] In August 1779 he embarked on his first serious commitment as an observer: the search for 'double stars' that might help in the long-sought-for determination of the distances of the nearest stars.

To a person walking through a landscape, the trees around him appear to move, and those near appear to move more than those further away: how much a stationary object appears to move is an indication of how near it is. Since the Earth is in orbit around the Sun, each star should appear to us to move, and the more so the nearer it is; and since the diameter of the Earth's orbit is known, measurement of this apparent movement ('annual parallax') will reveal the actual distance of the star. However, by the 1770s not a single example of annual parallax had as yet been detected. Estimates of stellar distances had been made on the assumption that Sirius (for example) was physically similar to the Sun, and appeared fainter only because of its remoteness. Arguing along these lines, Newton had shown that Sirius could well be a million or so times further than the Sun, a distance so great that its annual parallax would be tiny;[144] and to detect such a minute movement that took place only gradually over a period of months seemed well-nigh impossible. Atmospheric refraction, the warping of the instrument-mounting as a result of climatic changes, the effect of the aberration of light, these and similar complications would almost certainly swamp the tiny apparent movement of the star.

Galileo had popularized a plausible way out of the difficulty.[145] If two stars chanced to lie in similar directions from Earth, but one was near and the other distant, then the distant star would have a negligible parallax and could serve as a quasi-fixed reference point from which to measure the parallax of the nearer star. If the two stars appeared from Earth to be so close that at first glance they appeared as one (so forming a 'double star'), then refraction and the other complications would affect them equally and so would have no net effect.

In late January 1778 William used some pages of his Journal to write himself a short treatise setting out the merits of the double star method of detecting annual parallax.[146] The method of course required that the two stars were at very different distances; and it was in some ways fortunate that he did not yet know of a recent paper by John Michell[147] pointing out that the number of double stars is so great that they cannot all occur by chance alignments, but that most must be companions in space (and therefore at the same distance from Earth).

William had already come across examples of double stars. As early as 9 April 1774 he had encountered Mizar in the Great Bear,[148] which had been known to be double since the mid-seventeenth century. On 28 January 1778, within hours of penning his little treatise, he examined Sirius, brightest of the stars and perhaps the nearest, in the hope of finding a faint neighbour, but he was disappointed; a week later he failed in a similar examination of Procyon. Finally, on 17 August 1779, shortly before moving to 19 New King Street (now the home of the Herschel Museum), he embarked on his first major undertaking as an observer: a systematic "review" of all the brighter stars in order to identify those that were indeed double.[149]

In time William's collection of double stars would run into hundreds, and he thereby introduced into astronomy the approach of the natural historian. He had himself been introduced to this type of investigation of the world around us — so alien to astronomers brought up on Newton's mathematics — by his youngest brother Dietrich. In late July 1777 Dietrich had absconded from the family home in Hanover, and William had had to drop what he was about and set off from Bath is an attempt to head him off before the lad was able to implement his plan of voyaging to distant parts. But Dietrich's scheme quickly unravelled, and by the end of August he was in Bath with William, Caroline and Alexander. A gifted musician like all the boys of the family, Dietrich happily spent a profitable two years with his siblings; and during this time he introduced William to his hobby of entomology, and to the approach of the natural historian. Hitherto the objects studied by astronomers had been few in number and each was an individual known by its proper name: the Sun, the Moon, the planets and their satellites, comets each identified by the year when it appeared, stars like Sirius or Procyon. In complete contrast, William revolutionized astronomy by imitating the natural historian, who collects great numbers of unnamed specimens and classifies them. His collection of double stars and their classification (according to their degree of separation) would introduce into astronomy a wholly new methodology.

On the very first night of his review William was rewarded with a remarkable coup: the discovery that the Pole Star is itself a double. So exquisite was the mirror of William's 7-ft reflector that it would be some time before any other observer would be able to confirm his claim.[150]

We do not know where it was that William had first encountered the use of double stars as a possible way to measure annual parallax. It may have cropped up in conversation with professional astronomers, for his scientific isolation was coming to an end. He had been in touch with Professor Thomas Hornsby of Oxford as early as 1774, and in 1777 a Bath neighbour had brought the Astronomer Royal, Nevil Maskelyne, to see him. Late in December 1779 he made the acquaintance of

William Watson, Jr, a local physician and Fellow of the Royal Society, who was to prove his staunchest ally.[151] William had spent only three months at 19 New King Street and was now at 27 Rivers Street. Watson introduced him to the newly-formed Bath Philosophical Society, whose premises were also in Rivers Street, and there he met congenial spirits and cut his scientific teeth. In 1780 alone he somehow found time to prepare no fewer than twenty-six papers on a variety of topics to be read to the society.[152]

He returned to 19 New King Street early in March 1781, and it was on the 13th, while he was engaged in his review of the brighter stars, that he came across a "curious either nebulous star or perhaps a comet" near ζ Tauri. He returned to the object four days later, and found that it had already moved position relative to stars in the same field of view. It was therefore not a true star, which would have been so distant as to seem motionless, but a nearby member of the solar system.[153] Watson communicated William's announcement of his discovery to the Royal Society in London, and on 3 May William attended a meeting of the Society and met Sir Joseph Banks, their President and a man who had the ear of the King himself.[154]

It was a sign of the extraordinary quality of William's telescope, that neither Maskelyne at Greenwich, nor Hornsby at Oxford, could distinguish the object from an ordinary star, even though they had professionally-made instruments at their disposal. And because William did not yet know how to define the position of a celestial body, it was some time before either man could be sure which of the objects in that particular region of sky was somehow special. Within weeks of the discovery Maskelyne inclined to the view that it was indeed a planet in a near-circular orbit, and if so it would be the first to be discovered since the dawn of history; as much as a year later, Hornsby still preferred to think of it as a comet.[155] Whatever the truth of the matter, the discovery was significant enough for William to be honoured in November 1781 with the Copley Medal of the Royal Society, and to be elected a Fellow soon afterwards. In January 1782 the Society received his first catalogue of no fewer than 269 double stars,[156] many of which defied resolution in the best telescopes of other observers. It was evident that an astronomical talent of quite exceptional quality had arrived on the scene: the discovery of the planet/comet was an isolated *tour de force* never to be repeated; the unprecedented list of double stars signalled an observer using superior instrumentation with long-term commitment.

William's talent was exceptional, but it was untutored in the conventions of scientific discourse. Two of his early papers to the Bath society reported his observations on the heights of mountains on the Moon. Watson thought William's conclusions worthy of forwarding to the Royal Society, but Nevil Maskelyne, on behalf of the Committee on Papers, asked for further elucidation. This the author was happy to supply. But unfortunately, William chose also to enlarge on what had been no more than a brief remark concerning "the great probability, not to say absolute certainty" of the Moon's being inhabited. This extended polemic was seen as inappropriate, being wholly irrelevant to the scientific matter at issue, and the added passage had to be excised before the paper appeared in *Philosophical Transactions*.[157] But William continued to believe in lunar inhabitants, and in solar ones as well: he later developed a theory whereby there are gaps in the blazing exterior of the Sun, and these gaps enable us to see (as 'sunspots') the dark inner spherical shield that protects the inhabitants from the heat.

William's ignorance of the customs governing scientific discourse was again exposed in the lengthy paper "On the Parallax of the Fixed Stars" that explained the motivation behind his search for double stars. It was read to the Royal Society on 6 December 1781. Watson afterwards warned him that one critic described the paper as "a flighty one", adding that "Dr Blagden told me he thought some part of your paper too elementary".[158] William had included a long description of his micrometer, and Watson reported that this had been described as smacking of "charletanerie".[159] More damaging was his mention in passing of "when I magnified 6450 times", he supposing such a claim to be in no need of justification. Watson put him right on this: "Opticians think it no small matter, if they sell a Telescope wch will magnify 60 or 100 times, & here comes one who pretends to have made some, which will magnify above 6000 times, is this credible?" How big, critics asked, would a star appear at such a magnification, and how rapidly would it cross his field of view?[160] To make matters worse, his early observations of the planet/comet were found to be seriously at fault. Alexander Aubert, a respected amateur astronomer who could appreciate William's achievements, wrote him a letter of consolation:

> Go on my dear Sir with courage, mind not a few barking, jealous little puppies, a little time will clear up the matter & if it lies in my power you shall not be sent to Bedlam [Bethlehem, the lunatic asylum] alone for I incline much to be of the party.[161]

While William was stumbling over his first steps in the national scientific forum, back home he was encountering a major setback in his ambitions to acquire a telescope of unprecedented "light gathering power", one that was intended to give him sight of very distant and therefore very faint objects. He began to plan the monster in January 1781. He decided that a focal length of 30 feet was the maximum for which he could guarantee a stable geometrical relationship between the two mirrors; drawing on what he read in Smith's *Opticks* and what he had learned from experience, "I consulted only my own powers of workmanship and supposing I could manage a speculum [mirror] of four feet diameter, fixed upon that as the size".[162] Such a mirror would be far beyond anything currently in existence, and would have 16 times the surface area of the mirrors of the 20-ft. The cost of so much metal was a worrying consideration.

It would also be essential to get the composition right, so as to avoid a mirror that was brittle, or had a granulated surface. He tried various mixtures, and by late February decided that he was on the right track. But the trials were expensive,

"Nor indeed have I patience to wait for uncertain results".

The weight, and therefore the cost, of a 3-ft mirror would be far less that one of 4-ft, and so on 26 February William decided to be content with this smaller size. He approached the various founders of both Bath and Bristol and asked if they would undertake the casting, only to discover that the task was beyond them. In no way deterred, "I had a furnace and melting oven built in a proper room on the ground of my house", so that he could do the casting for himself. What his neighbours in the terrace thought of the likelihood of the entire street going up in flames is not recorded.

In the spring and summer small-scale experiments in the composition of the metal continued. Meanwhile, the wooden support was planned and constructed (although the tube itself may never have been finished).[163] William's long but narrow back garden faced southwest, and gave him a view of the sky in the meridian from 10° above the horizon up to the zenith. The mounting consisted of three stout poles each set vertically in brick supports that were 4 feet from each other. The poles were joined at the top by a circular cap, in the centre of which was a pivot from which projected an arm that extended a little beyond the circle of the poles. At the end of the arm were pulleys and ropes that could raise and lower the front of the tube. Within the three poles was an observing platform with safety railings, and this could be raised or lowered (rather like a modern lift) so as to bring the observer level with the eyepiece.[164]

This sounds reminiscent of the Heath Robinson apparatus of modern fiction. If the reflector was to reach stars near the zenith, the poles would have needed to be some 30 feet in height. It is difficult to believe that an arm extended sideways from the top of such poles could have supported a tube itself some 30 feet in length and 3 feet in diameter. And while minor adjustments in altitude and azimuth were to be made by the observer as in the 20-ft, major movements of the tube would have involved huge physical effort. The base of the tube would have been near the wooden poles for observations close to the zenith, but approaching 30 feet away from the poles for observations of stars near the horizon. The mirror was to have an iron ring at the back so that it could be removed from the tube by crane, but even without the mirror the manhandling of the tube would have been a daunting prospect. Perhaps it was as well that the apparatus was never put to the test.

The mould for the mirror was made in part of horse dung, and Caroline, Alexander, and even Watson were recruited to pound the dung into a suitable consistency. In his memorandum for 11 August 1781, William notes laconically, "I cast the great metal". His "Experiments" enlarge on this. The molten metal ran "very quietly" into the mould; but when the mould was nearly full, a crack appeared, and the resultant mirror was too thin on one side. But in any case the mirror itself cracked, and this William interpreted as due to its faulty composition. It is more likely that he did not appreciate that allowing the exterior to cool too fast would set up stresses in the metal. As Watson afterwards told him, "I think you must contrive some method to ensure its cooling gradually, Mr Michell you know put his in an oven, where it remaind unseen and untouch'd for several Days".[165]

A few days later, William varied the composition and tried again.

> When everything was in readiness we put our 537,9 pounds of metal into the melting oven and gradually heated it; before it was sufficiently fluid for casting we perceived that some quantity began to drop through the bottom of the furnace into the fire. The crack soon increased and the metal came out so fast that it ran out of the ash hole which was not lower than the stone floor of the room, when it came upon the pavement the flags began to crack and some of them to blow up, so that we found it necessary to keep at a proper distance and suffer the metal to take its own course.[166]

Caroline gives a hint of the true drama: "... both my Brothers, and the caster and his men were obliged to run out at opposite doors."[167] At this, even William admitted (temporary) defeat. The scarred floor is still to be seen.

Meanwhile the amateur astronomer had been forced to spend most of his waking hours in his profession of music: only four days after confirming that the "curious" object of 13 March 1781 had moved and therefore should urgently be drawn to the attention of professional astronomers, he was directing an oratorio in Bath, with a repeat performance two days later in Bristol.

Despite the competing pressures, the oratorios were a success. But a year later, when William had been alerted to an impending summons to Court that he knew might transform his life, music was receiving scant attention. On 7 March 1782 the *Bath Chronicle* announced that the oratorio to be given in Bath on Wednesday in Passion Week would be *Jephtha*. The following week this was amended to *Samson*, and the following week, only days before the actual performance, to *Judas Maccabaeus* — signs of chaos, and near-panic, on William's part as director.[168]

The Bristol performance that followed soon after was nothing short of a disaster. In the morning, when a chaise was ready to take William and Caroline to the rehearsal with the musical parts for nearly a hundred performers, William was deep in conversation with Watson concerning the expected summons to Court, and it was then that a nephew of his arrived from Windsor with "confirmation that his Oncle was expected with his instrument [the 7-ft reflector with which he had discovered the planet or comet] in town". William had thoughts only for London, and it was left to Caroline to assemble the parts as best she could.[169] Not surprisingly, the standard of the performance later that day was lamentable. As a letter in a Bristol newspaper put it:

> Perhaps no audience was ever more impos'd on, or worse treated than that which Thursday night attended the performance of the *Messiah* at your theatre.
>
> Many Gentlemen who went principally with a wish of hearing Mr. Tenducci, found themselves at the drawing up of the curtain (and not till then) disappointed — Hand-bills indeed were printed; but they were confin'd wholly to

the company of the boxes — and so were only printed with a view to save the Manager's credit — It was expected and hop'd that some exertions would have been made by Mr. Rauzzini to compensate for Mr. Tenducci's absence — but that performer satisfied himself with singing one song, and joining, now and then, in a chorus. — Such was Mr. Herschel's eagerness to conclude the performance, that songs — duets — choruses, were omitted — the audience disgusted — and the band thrown into confusion. The first violin led off one air, while the violoncello had begun the accompaniment of another.

The chorus singers were repeatedly at a loss whether to stand up or keep their seats; and Mr. Rauzzini had almost trampled Miss Storer to death, in endeavouring to sing from Mr. Croft's paper, instead of his own, which neither himself or the conductor of the band knew anything of.[170]

A week later William responded with an apology for the change of singer and the delay in distributing handbills (though he ignored the other criticisms).

But the lesson had been learned. When William directed another performance of *Messiah*, on 1 May 1782, to inaugurate a new organ at the largest parish church in Bath, the choir was strongly reinforced, by choristers from Salisbury along with the famous singers of Lady Huntingdon's Chapel; and this time the performance was a success.[171]

Meanwhile William's scientific admirers had been exploring ways in which he might be relieved of the need to earn his living through music and allowed instead to dedicate all his energies to astronomy. Was there a salaried position to which he might be appointed? If not, the only hope lay in royal patronage.

There was no prospect of William's being appointed to either Oxford or Greenwich, for Hornsby and Maskelyne were in their prime, and in any case William was neither an academic nor a mathematician. But in 1768 the King had embarked on the construction of a private observatory at Kew, near London, specifically in order to view the transit of Venus across the face of the Sun that was to occur the following year. He equipped it with instruments by leading makers — Adams, Shelton and Sisson — and appointed as Superintendent his former tutor, Stephen C. T. Demainbray.[172] The viewing of the transit was a success, although the observations were never published.[173] Thereafter, however, Demainbray had looked on his post as a sinecure, and limited himself to recording the weather,[174] checking the clocks that provided the time at Parliament and other public buildings in London,[175] and perhaps giving a few lectures. By 1782 he was in his seventies and frail in health.

Here was a post ideally suited to William, in effect that of astronomer to the Court with freedom to pursue his research except when the Royal Family wished to profit from his knowledge. But how best to direct the King's mind in this direction? A precedent for the discovery of William's 'star' — by now increasingly recognized as the first planet to be found since the dawn of history — was Galileo's discovery of the moons of Jupiter, and he had named them for the Medici family and been handsomely rewarded. Banks saw here an example to be followed: William should name his 'star' for the King, and his friends would suggest the post at Kew — when it fell vacant — as a suitable reward.

This well-laid scheme was overtaken by events: Demainbray died before the naming of the 'star' could be arranged. As Banks wrote to Watson on 23 February 1782:

> I wished the new star, so remarkable a phenomenon, to have been sacrificed somehow to the King. I thought how snug a place his Majesty's astronomer at Richmond [i.e., Kew] is and have frequently talked to the King of Mr Herschel's extraordinary abilities. I knew Demainbray was old but as the Devil will have it he died last night. I was at the [royal] Levy this morning but did not receive any hopes. I fear [the time] has passed by which a well timed compliment might have helped if the old gentleman had chose to live long enough to have allowed us to have paid it.[176]

The King's unwillingness to appoint William to Kew was, it later transpired, because he had already promised the post to Demainbray's son.[177] An honourable man, the King would not go back on his word; yet the promise left him in a quandary as to just how else he could make it possible for William to give up music for astronomy. George had not needed Banks to tell him of William's remarkable discovery: he had discussed it with Demainbray months before.[178] The King was more than happy to have the object named after him, but how was he to respond? While he pondered the problem, he would be glad to meet the man of whom he had heard so much, and to see for himself how the heavens appeared when viewed through William's telescope. And he said as much to Sophia's son, George Griesbach. As Watson told Banks on 27 March 1782,

> It gives me likewise great pleasure to be able to inform you that since Dr Demainbray's death, the King has again twice spoken to Mr Griesbach in relation to Mr Herschel, & told him that Mr Herschel was to come to him as soon as the Concerts at Bath were over. These are very encouraging circumstances, & make me still hope that the King has some notion of making him Demainbray's successor....[179]

In his Memoranda for April 1782, William notes that he "was informed by several that the King awaited" him.[180] Watson told Banks early that month:

> The King the first time he saw him [Griesbach] at Windsor asked him after his *uncles* at Bath, & how Mr Herschel's telescope went. To which Mr Griesbach answered that his Uncle was preparing them for the inspection of his Majesty. The King, you see, has very often made enquiries after Mr H since Dr Demainbray's Death, & indeed, I find since, oftner than I have mentioned to you, which makes me hope he has him in his eye yet....[181]

On 10 May Colonel John Walsh wrote to William:

> In a conversation I had the Honour to hold with His Majesty the 30th ult°

concerning You and Your memorable Discovery of a new Planet, I took occasion to mention that You had a twofold claim, as a native of Hanover and a Resident of Great Britain, where the Discovery was made, to be permitted to name the Planet from his Majesty. His Majesty has since been pleased to ask me when You would be in Town....[182]

William's last commitment for the music season, apart from the teaching of private pupils, was to play the organ at St Margaret's Chapel on Whit Sunday, 19 May;[183] one of his anthems was performed, and Caroline sang the treble solo. On the Monday he took the coach to London where he was to stay with Dr William Watson Sr in Lincoln's Inn Fields.[184] He had devised a portable stand for the 7-ft,[185] and an ambitious list of double stars to show the King.[186]

How he spent the days immediately following we do not know, but on the Saturday he dined with Colonel Walsh in the company of Maskelyne and Aubert.[187] Aubert had recently succeeded in confirming William's claim that the Pole Star was a double.[188] He was one of William's loyal allies, and in 1786 made him the exceptional gift of a 'regulator' (precision clock) by John Shelton, which keeps time to this day.[189]

On Sunday the 26th William had an audience with the King and Queen, to whom he presented a drawing of the solar system in which the new planet doubtless featured prominently. His Majesty "received me very graciously. The King said that my telescope in three weeks was to go to Richmond and meanwhile to be put up at Greenwich".[190] At Greenwich it would be professionally tested against the instruments of the Royal Observatory; at Kew the King himself could compare it with the ones he had bought for his own observatory.

At this stage it seems that the King had said nothing about Demainbray's successor, and William — and certainly Watson — were under the impression that the Superintendency was still undecided.[191] But first the Greenwich trial lay ahead, in which William's home-made reflector would seek endorsement from the friendly but demanding Astronomer Royal. Accordingly, later on the Sunday William took his reflector to Greenwich. To Caroline he wrote: "Tell Alexander that everything looks very likely as if I were to stay here.... My having seen the King need not be kept secret, but about my staying here it will be best not to say anything but only I must remain here till His Maj. has observed the Planets with my telescope."[192] Since he warned Caroline in the same letter that she was unlikely to see him in less than a month, the "staying here" presumably refers to a permanent appointment that William anticipated, and this was no doubt the Superintendency at Kew.

On Wednesday the 29th William assembled his telescope at Greenwich, ready for the trial. He took the opportunity to assess the opposition: "I tryed the acchromatic telescope of Dr Maskelyne ... with [magnification] 920 very strong aberration & ill defined. My reflector in tollerable fine weather is hardly so bad with 3168. I tried also Dr Mask. 6 feet Reflector of Shorts but it would bear no higher power than 3 or 400, upon α Lyrae."[193] The omens were favourable. On the Friday he attended the King's regular concert at which George Griesbach performed. "The King spoke to me as soon as he saw me, and kept me in conversation for half an hour."[194] The next two nights William was at Greenwich. On Saturday 1 June he observed with Maskelyne and his assistant Joseph Lindley.[195] William was more than pleased with the outcome. "D^r M tried to see the small star of ε Bootis in his Achromatic but with the deepest comon night piece could not perceive it. Nor could I see it with the same piece. We saw it both extremely well in mine."[196] On the Sunday they were joined by Aubert, with equally satisfactory results. A delighted William reported to his sister next day:

> We have compared our telescopes together, and mine was found superior to any of the Royal Observatory. Double stars which they could not see with their instruments I had the pleasure to show them very plainly, and my mechanism is so much approved of that Dr Maskelyne has already ordered a model to be taken from mine and a stand made by it to his reflector. He is, however, now so much out of love with his instrument that he begins to doubt whether it *deserves* a new stand.[197]

On the Tuesday William dined at Lord Palmerston's, and on the Wednesday with Banks.[198] It seems he must have gone on to Greenwich after dinner with Banks, for he discovered a new double star that night.[199] On Thursday the 6th he was at the King's concert. "As soon as the King saw me he came and spoke to me, about my telescope but he has not yet fixed a time when he will see it."[200] A possible reason for the delay was the Court mourning to begin at the weekend, and Caroline was to send her brother suitable clothes. William left his 7-ft at Greenwich for the weekend, and went to visit Aubert. Now it was his turn to make trial:

> ... we have tried his Instruments upon the double stars and they would not at all perform what I had expected, so that I have no doubt but mine is better than any Mr Aubert has; and if that is the case I can now say that I absolutely have the best telescopes that were ever made.[201]

Which was no more than the truth.

For the rest of June, William languished in London waiting on the King's pleasure, and making occasional visits to Greenwich. On Tuesday the 11th and Friday the 14th he was there making observations, and on the Saturday a distinguished company once more assembled at the Observatory to look through his telescope: Maskelyne, Aubert, Playfair (perhaps John Playfair, the Scottish mathematician and geologist), Professor Antony Shepherd of Cambridge, and John Arnold the great watchmaker. On the Sunday William seems to have been able to observe alone with only Lindley for company, and he was again at work on each of the following three nights.[202]

The 7-ft was to remain at Greenwich for some days more, but we are poorly informed as to how William spent the time, for he relayed news to Bath in letters to Watson that are lost. Watson for his part was fearful that his friend's diffidence was causing him to miss an opportunity that might never come again. Banks had promised to approach the King on William's behalf, but if necessary William himself must make a move.

> The King has shewn you every outward mark in his behaviour of predilection for you. But he might justly think that he ought previously to know that you are willing to accept of the place, before he makes you the offer. For want of knowing precisely your situation & wishes, how should he know but that you might be from your situation at Bath in such flourishing circumstances, as to make you above accepting of the Post of his Astronomer at Kew.... I should certainly take the first opportunity ... humbly to request that you might succeed the late Dr Demainbray at Kew provided his Majesty thought of appointing [a] successor, & that you should look upon such a Post as the most happy event of your Life.[203]

William's reply managed to pacify Watson, who replied on the 23rd: "you are perfectly right to remain quietly in Town & abide the event...." But Watson was concerned that Hornsby, who had not been at Greenwich to see for himself the excellence of William's reflector, had only an indifferent opinion of William because of mistakes the inexperienced amateur had made in his reporting of the positions and movement of the comet or planet that he had discovered. Hornsby, Watson insisted, must be converted into an ally before he had the opportunity to offer the King a damaging assessment; and if this meant delaying the Kew meeting with the King, so be it.[204]

We hear nothing more of the Hornsby problem, which probably existed more in the mind of Watson than in reality. As we have seen, Hornsby had met William as early as 1774 and had gone out of his way to be helpful,[205] and as a university teacher he was no doubt able to discern a talent masked by limitations of education. But Watson's appeals to William to take the initiative began to bear fruit. Writing on 29 June, Watson says he is glad that William is

> well convinced of the necessity that the King should be apply'd to. He has done every thing on his side to shew his partiality towards you & it cannot be expected that he should condescend to offer before he knows that his offer will be accepted.[206]

He approves of William's plan to approach Dr William Heberden as an intermediary. Heberden had been personal physician to the Queen since 1761, and if Banks failed to make the promised approach to the King then Heberden would be a second friend at Court.

It is likely that the King's reluctance to make an offer stemmed not so much from the need to maintain royal dignity in negotiations as from uncertainty as to what form of offer he could reasonably make. Caroline later recounted[207] that the possibility of her brother's being astronomer to the Court in Hanover was mooted, but as the proposed salary was only £100 per annum — less than a quarter the income William was currently making in Bath — we hear no more of this. But the ideal solution now occurred to the King. Not only George Griesbach but his brother Henry were members of Queen Charlotte's band, entertaining guests during dinner at Buckingham House or Windsor Castle.[208] To have an astronomer living near Windsor under royal patronage would solve the problem of how to entertain guests at the Castle when dinner was over, as well as guaranteeing instruction for the King when he was in residence. But was William equal to the task? To decide this question the would-be professional astronomer was invited, not to Kew, but to Windsor. Accordingly, on Tuesday 2 July William set up his reflector at Queen's Lodge:

> This evening His Majesty and all the Royal Family observed Jupiter Saturn and several double Stars with my 7-ft Reflector. His Majesty had ordered three of his Instruments (viz a 10 or 12 f^t Achromatic of Dollond's a 3½ Achromatic a Short's reflector) to be brought in order that they might be compared with mine; and my Telescope shewed the heavenly bodies much more distinct than the other Instruments. His Majesty saw ε Bootis with [magnification] 460 and the Pole Star with 932. The Queen found the Newtonian construction very convenient.[209]

His delighted letter next day to Caroline tells us more:

> Last night the King, the Queen, the Prince of Wales, the Princess Royal, Princess Sophia, Princess Augusta, &c, Duke of Montague, Dr Hebberdon [Heberden], Mons Luc &c. &c, saw my telescope and it was a very fine evening. My Instrument gave a general satisfaction; the King has very good eyes & enjoys Observations with Telescopes exceedingly.
>
> This evening as the King & Queen are gone to Kew, the Princesses were desirous of seeing my Telescope, but wanted to know if it was possible to see without going out on the grass, and were much pleased when they heard that my telescope could be carried into any place they liked best to have it. About 8 o'clock it was moved into the Queen's Apartments and we waited some time in hopes of seeing Jupiter or Saturn. Mean while I shewed the Princesses & several other Ladies that were present, the Speculum, the Micrometers, the movements of the Telescope, and other things that seemed to excite their curiosity. When the evening appeared to be totally unpromising, I proposed an artificial Saturn as an object since we could not have the real one. I had beforehand prepared this little piece, as I guessed from the appearance of the weather in the afternoon [that] we should have no stars to look at. This being accepted with great pleasure, I had the lamps lighted up which illuminated the picture of a Saturn (cut out in pasteboard) at the bottom of the garden wall.
>
> The effect was fine and so natural that the best astronomer might have been deceived. Their Royal Highnesses and other Ladies seemed to be much pleased with the artifice. I remained in the Queen's Apartments with the Ladies till about half after ten, when in conversation with them I found them extremely well

instructed in every subject that was introduced and they seem to be the most amiable Characters. To-morrow evening they hope to have better luck & nothing will give me greater happiness than to be able to shew them some of those beautiful objects with which the Heavens are so gloriously ornamented.[210]

In short, the trial had been a great success. William and the King were both possessed of a natural charm and got on well together, and no doubt the encounter gave William ample opportunity to hint at how pleased he would be to be able to dedicate himself to astronomy. And so it was that within days the King sent to William an emissary, General Heinrich Wilhelm von Freytag.[211] William was invited to become astronomer to the Court at Windsor with a 'pension' of £200 per annum, free to pursue his researches, his only obligation being to live close to the Castle and to be available to the Royal Family and their guests on request. Towards the end of the year William duly wrote a formal letter to Banks naming his planet Georgium Sidus,[212] echoing the name of Medicea Sidera that Galileo gave to the moons of Jupiter when dedicating them to his patron. But Continental astronomers preferred the name Uranus, and that is how we know the planet today.

Watson expressed his delight at the news of the pension, and encouraged William to ask Freytag to intercede with the King should he have any counter-requests of his own.[213] Possibly William took the opportunity to ask permission to supplement his income (and incidentally to fund experiments in construction techniques) by making telescopes for sale.

William, as Caroline tells us, had had no hesitation in accepting the King's offer, for he could not bear the thought of returning to the dreary round of musical performances and the endless lessons for pupils without ability.[214] For some days he lodged with George Griesbach while his 7-ft remained at Queen's Lodge, and on the 9th and on each of the six nights from the 18th to the 23rd of July he used it to continue his search for double stars.[215] His days he evidently spent searching for accommodation that had buildings for workshops and space to erect his telescopes, and he quickly found what he wanted in the village of Datchet, a mile and a half to the east of the castle.[216] This done, he returned to Bath where with the help of Caroline and Alexander he packed his instruments and belongings in a matter of days, and arranged their transport to Datchet. On the night of 1 August all three siblings slept in the inn next to the church at Datchet, and they awoke on the 2nd to find the wagon had safely arrived.[217] The next evening William made his first observations from his new home.[218] There was no time to lose: nearly 44 years of age, he was at last a professional astronomer.

1782–1822: ASTRONOMER TO THE COURT AT WINDSOR

To Caroline, her new home was "the ruins of a place".[219] Certainly it took William and Alexander two whole months to get it into some semblance of order, after which Alexander had to return to Bath. But even when William and Caroline quit the property nearly three years later, "there was not one room but where the rain came through the ceiling".[220] In their first weeks William was periodically summoned to take his 7-ft reflector to Windsor Castle, with all the expense and disruption this entailed. On 30 August "His Majesty saw several Nebulae" including M 11 and M 31,[221] and on 3 September a "minute double star" in Bootes.[222] On 12 October "I shew'd his Majesty the Moon & the Nebula in the Crown of Antinous with my new 10f Speculum & stand upon three supports".[223] It is not clear whether William took this sizeable reflector to the Castle, but certainly on 1 December 1782 "The King came to see my 20 feet Telescope and other instruments in the evening". And so it was that within four months of their arrival,[224] William and Caroline found themselves playing host to their sovereign in their dilapidated home.

In the second week of December, William returned to Bath to retrieve the fragments of metal from the ill-fated 3-ft mirror, and he and Alexander took the opportunity to cast another mirror for the 20-ft. This proved a wise precaution, for on 1 January the mirror William was currently using cracked in the extreme cold.[225]

Datchet saw the start of Caroline's own career as an observer. Equipped with only a simple refractor, she was soon finding examples of the nebulae and clusters that had been catalogued by the French comet-hunter Charles Messier (because he was finding them a distraction), and then she began to discover clusters that were previously unknown. Impressed, William started himself to 'sweep' for nebulae with a modest achromatic; but then he realized that unlike comets, which are here today and gone tomorrow, nebulae and clusters are permanent features of the night sky, and will await their turn for examination with a major telescope. And his own 'large' 20-ft, with 18-inch mirrors and provision for the observer to work in safety, was nearing completion.

The reflector came into service in October 1783, and William attempted at first to use it single-handedly to sweep for nebulae. But experience soon showed that when, after a few minutes of observations, he used artificial light to make a record of what he had seen, it would be some time before his eyes were again adapted to the dark. This slowed the work unacceptably. At the end of the year, therefore, he recruited Caroline to be his amanuensis: he did the observing and she the recording. For two decades they systematically examined the sky visible from Windsor in the search for nebulae, albeit with diminishing enthusiasm on William's part. Finally, in 1802, William called a halt, with the work almost — but not quite — completed.[226]

While at Bath he had made telescopes *gratis* for family and friends — Caroline, Alexander, Dietrich, Watson[227] — but the situation had changed when he settled near Windsor on a pension of less than half the income he had been earning through music. In addition his expenses had increased, for he was anxious to build a truly massive telescope with large mirrors that would collect the light from distant and therefore faint objects, and so allow him to study their nature. Precision instruments like the 7-ft called for a huge investment in patience during the grinding and polishing, but the raw materials were relatively inexpensive. Big reflectors cost serious money, for the purchase of wood, brass and 'speculum' metal, and for the wages of the workmen of many different trades. William was venturing into unknown territory, and even the experiments that might show the best procedures for him to adopt were themselves expensive.

King George had no doubt realized that the pension he was offering William was modest (Watson, when told of the terms, commented: "Never bought Monarch honour so cheap!"[228]); and in the autumn of 1783 he authorized William to supplement it by making telescopes for sale, and himself placed an order for five 10-ft reflectors.[229]

> The goodness of my telescopes being generally known I was desired by the King to get some made for those who wished to have them. Getting the woodwork done by his Majesty's cabinet maker, I fitted up five 10 feet telescopes for the King, and very soon found a great demand for 7 feet reflectors. This business, in the end, not only proved very lucrative but also enabled me to make expensive experiments for polishing mirrors by machinery.

It was a generous act on the part of the King, for although one telescope was for Windsor Castle, a second for the royal observatory at Kew, and a third for Göttingen University (a favourite 'good cause' on the part of the King in his capacity as Elector of Hanover), he had no idea what to do with the other two, and eventually gave one to the Duke of Marlborough and the other to the Saxony ambassador, Count de Brühl.[230] William was now launched on a career as one of the great telescope-builders of all time.

At first most of the commissions came from astronomers both professional and amateur, but later, as his fame spread, the crowned heads of Europe began to compete to own one of his reflectors.[231] The most expensive item on his price list would be a 40-ft reflector, though fortunately none was ever ordered and so his bluff was never called.[232]

In June 1785, after nearly three years at Datchet, William and Caroline moved the short distance to a property in Old Windsor known as Clay Hall. The castle, a mile and a half to the northwest, could clearly be seen from their new home. But they soon found that the owner, Mrs Laura Keppel,[233] "a litigious woman" according to William and "a fiery furnace" according to Horace Walpole, demanded increases in rent when William made improvements to the property. Nine months later, therefore, they moved to Slough, then a little village a couple of miles north of Windsor on the London–Bath road, and settled into the house where William would one day die.

The property was owned by a neighbour, Mrs Elizabeth Baldwin. Her late husband had been a merchant in the City of London, and she was well provided for. Another of her properties was occupied by her married daughter Mary and Mary's husband, the wealthy John Pitt; and although the Pitt home was in the next village of Upton, the houses were in the same parish and the Pitts' land bordered that of the Herschels. Soon the Pitts and the Herschels were warm friends; much too warm for Caroline's liking, for when John Pitt died in the summer of 1786, William began to pay court to his widow.

The obstacle to their marriage lay in Mary's unwillingness to give up her home at Upton. It was agreed, therefore, that the couple would live in Upton, but that William would (of course) conduct his astronomy at Slough, the location of both his telescopes and his assistant Caroline. But on reflection, Mary decided that William "would be principally at [Slough], and that Miss Herschel would be mistress of the concern", and she broke off the engagement.[234] Eventually a curious compromise was agreed: they would maintain both houses, with two maidservants in each, and a footman to go back and forth, while Caroline was to move into apartments over the workshops at Slough.[235] Even more curious was William's decision then to take soundings among his friends and fellow-astronomers, to see if they approved of his proposed marriage, for the stars would now be competing with Mary for William's attentions at night. Watson reported back that opinion was generally in favour, and he for his part thought that astronomy would in fact benefit if William adopted a less stressful lifestyle.[236] It was an odd way to enter into a partnership that would secure William a charming and loving wife, financial prosperity beyond his dreams, and in due course a brilliant son who would one day become his father's apprentice and heir in astronomy.

On 8 May 1788 they were married at Upton Church, a modest building noted today primarily because it houses their tomb. Before long the newly-weds abandoned the compromise, and established themselves at Slough. A decade later, on the death of Mary's mother, they were to inherit the property.[237]

Hitherto William had been a driven man, obsessed by his current project, be it in music or astronomy. Now he could widen his horizons in human terms, and Mary was so well-off that he no longer needed to concern himself over money. The timing of his marriage was especially fortunate because back in the autumn of 1785 William and his allies had taken the momentous — and ill-judged — step of asking King George to fund the construction of a reflector with mirrors 4-ft in diameter that would enable it to penetrate deep into space (and perhaps settle the question of whether all nebulae were clusters of stars).

Hitherto William had funded his telescope-making out of his own pocket, drawing on the savings he had accumulated as a successful musician; but his income was now half what it had been in Bath, and the 'large' 20-ft had shown the importance of having a substantial — and expensive — mounting. A monster reflector was wholly beyond his means.

One of the visitors to Datchet had been his old ally, William Watson. Watson found his gifted friend hampered in his ambitions for lack of financial support, and he determined to rectify the situation. According to Caroline, Watson

> saw my Brother's difficulties and expressed great dissatisfaction. And on his return to Bath he met among the Visitors there several belonging to the Court ... to whom he gave his opinion concerning his Friend and his situation very

The painting (in the Herschel Family Archives) of the 'large' 20-ft, by Rev. Thomas Rackett (1755–1840), showing William in the observing chair. In its early weeks, the reflector was fixed in the meridian, and William dragged the tube from side to side, while standing on an observing platform as shown in the engraving published in 1794 (Bennett, 83). But the platform would have been cumbersome to raise and lower, and when the telescope was acting solely as a transit instrument William might prefer a simple observing chair, as shown here. The workman is seen raising and lowering the telescope by means of a windlass; a second windlass, to the workman's left, allowed him to raise or lower the chair. In November 1785, at the height of the sweeps for nebulae, John Smeaton visited William, and his letter to John Michell of 4 November 1785 (copy in RAS MS Radcliffe Hornsby 78) confirms that William was then using the chair. However, it may not have been possible for William to use the chair if he wished to use the telescope to sweep at high elevations, when the sweeps might range over as much as 5°, or when he wanted to avoid the loss of light resulting from use of the secondary mirror by peering directly into the tube (as had been done as early as 1728 by Jacques Lemaire, see *Dictionary of Scientific Biography*). William had tried this arrangement in November 1783 and introduced it permanently in October 1786 (Bennett, 85). The house in the painting does not appear to be that at Old Windsor and is not that at Slough, so it is probably our only representation of the property at Datchet, which William left in June 1785. The first evidence that the telescope could be rotated (as shown here) dates from September 1784 (Bennett, 86), and so the painting was probably completed between September 1784 and June 1785.

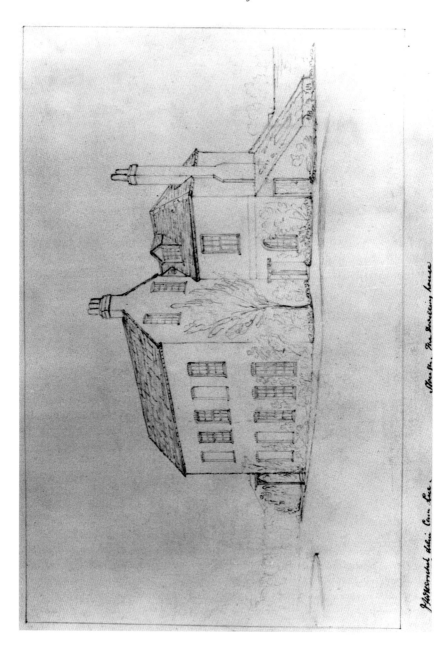

William's house at Slough, as drawn by his son John with a camera lucida. From the original in the Herschel Family Archives.

freely. In consequence of which, very soon after, my Brother had, through Sir J. Banks, the promise that 2000 pounds would be granted for enabling him to make himself an Instrument.[238]

William himself, writing long after the event, tells a similar story:

> ... my present situation being much more limited with regard to income than my former one at Bath, I thought it prudent to request the favour of the President of the R[oyal] S[ociety] to make an application to the King. His Majesty most graciously granted my petition.... It remained now only to fix upon the size of it, and having proposed to the King either a 30 or a 40 feet telescope His Majesty fixed upon the largest.[239]

Of course! Those who fund scientific research look for the best value for their money. But William was to pay heavily for his act of bravado in offering the King this choice of size.

George promised William £2000, equal to the expected capital costs plus the running costs for four years.[240] A decade later, when William offered similar reflectors for sale, his asking price for instrument plus mounting was no less than 8000 guineas.[241] This of course included a profit margin, but the contrast between £8400 and the £1395 capital cost cited in William's application makes it clear that William was hopelessly underestimating how much he would need from the King. Was this due to naïvety, or over-optimism — or the ploy familiar to modern astronomers whereby an initial and modest fund application is made, in the belief that the granting body will later cough up further funds rather than write off those already invested? If so, William's ploy would succeed, but the King would be alienated in the process, and it may be for this reason that William's knighthood had to await until 1816 and the Regency of the future George IV. Such an honour was by then long, long overdue: as Caroline later told John, "General Komarzewsky would say to your father, Why does not he (meaning King George III) make you Duke of Slough?"[242]

The estrangement was not entirely William's fault. The King had no conception of the immensity of the ground-breaking task William had set himself. Metal disks and other apparatus would have to be shipped up-river from London, and whole armies of workmen engaged locally. Yet as early as November 1785, only weeks after approving the grant, the King was demanding signs of tangible progress;[243] and the following summer, oblivious of the disruption this would cause, he insisted that William drop everything and personally travel to Göttingen and present the university with one of the 10-ft reflectors he had commissioned.[244]

By the summer of 1787 William could no longer hide from himself, or the King, that the project was in financial crisis. In particular, he realized that the mirror he had cast was too thin to keep its shape when tilted in the tube, and that a much thicker, heavier — and therefore more expensive — one was necessary. Diplomacy of a high order was now called for, but such was William's confidence in the

Miniature (in the Herschel Family Archives) of William as a young man, artist unknown. It was probably given to Caroline by William when he visited Hanover in 1764, and was later given by Caroline to John according to a note that now accompanies it.

Mary Herschel in March 1805, from a miniature on ivory by John Keenan, in the Herschel family archives. Mary's brother Thomas Baldwin admired it sufficiently to commission a matching miniature of himself two months later. Keenan came from Ireland, and from 1790 was active in London, Bath and elsewhere in southern England. From 1802 he worked in Windsor and in 1809 became court painter to Queen Charlotte. Between 1791 and 1815 he exhibited at the Royal Academy some sixty pictures, nearly all portraits. In 1817 he returned to Dublin.

justness of his cause that the letter he wrote on 18 July to a royal aide was almost peremptory in tone. He refers to his original grant application, and continues:

> As it was impossible to say exactly what sum might be sufficient to finish so grand a work, I now find that many of the parts take up much more time and labour of workmen, and more materials than I apprehended they would have taken, and that consequently my first estimate of the total expense will fall considerably short of the real amount.... I beg of you therefore to ask the King, whether it will please his Majesty that I should communicate the particulars of the further expence of the telescope to the President of the Royal Society, in order that he may, as before, take an opportunity to lay the same before the King, or whether his Majesty would order me to continue the workmen and apply from time to time for such sums as may be wanted....[245]

Whereas the King had understood he was making a once-only grant to cover both construction and running costs, William assumes he has been given a blank cheque, the only question being the procedural steps by which he should extract unspecified further funds from the royal coffers.

The King evidently decided it was time to see for himself what his initial grant had bought. A month later, on 17 August 1787, he descended in person on the Herschel home, accompanied by a vast retinue.[246] He was, it seems, in good humour. The tube of the great telescope lay on the ground, and the King and the Archbishop of Canterbury made to go inside. The Archbishop hesitated, whereupon the King encouraged him with "Come, my Lord Bishop, I will show you the way to Heaven".

It may well be that at the time of the visit the King did not appreciate the scale of the additional funds that William required, for he evidently left William with the impression that a formal application through Banks would be favourably received. Accordingly, William wrote off to Banks in buoyant mood, explaining that

> as it is his Majesty's intention further to support the construction and completion of this instrument as well as to provide for such necessary annual expenses as will be connected with its being kept up and serving for a series of observations, I shall lay before you an account of the things which are still wanting with an estimate of the expenses they may occasion.

He has thought it sufficient to put down the amounts "in a general way", though he assures Banks that these are based on detailed estimates. The total capital sum required — barring an unforeseen disaster to the great mirror — is £960 pounds. The annual running costs of £245 he will "by good management" seek to limit to £200. For his assistant, Caroline, he requests £50 per annum.[247]

Astonishingly, the King gave William all this and another £1000 besides. One might have suspected that the experienced Banks had discreetly taken the opportunity to increase the sum requested, so as to create a contingency fund; but the letter in the royal archives not only matches the accompanying Estimate of Expenses but is word-for-word the same as the copy of the letter in William's own papers: the King was asked for a lump sum of £960 and he gave £2000.[248]

Equally astonishing is it that the over-generous grant was made in the context of a blazing row between William and the King. The first hint of trouble comes in the tone of Banks's reply to William. Banks was so intimate a friend that he would soon be best man at William's wedding, yet his letter is curt and to the point:

> I have this moment seen the King who has granted all you ask but upon certain conditions which I must explain to you. Will you be so good as to come to me in Soho Square tomorrow as soon as convenient that we may finished this matter & that I may report to him before he sets out for Windsor.[249]

William had the ability to wipe unhappy memories from his mind, destroying the documentary evidence as he did so; and so it is that almost nothing survives as testimony to the row save a consoling letter from Watson to William, and a couple of sentences Caroline penned for family eyes only, forty years after the event:

> But there can be no harm in telling my own dear nephew, that I never felt satisfied with the support your father received towards his undertakings, and far less with the ungracious manner in which it was granted. For the last sum came with a message that more must never be asked for. (Oh! how degraded I felt even for myself whenever I thought of it!)[250]

Watson's long letter is dated 7 September 1787:

> ... I do most sincerely sympathize with you, & feel in some measure as you must feel at the unworthy treatment you (& I may add Science) has received. But I sincerely hope by the latter part of your letter that the Storm is past, & that the K— is brought by reflexion to know you ... a little better. For I am confident that no prince could have secured so much reputation at so small an expence, as has done his Majesty by the countenance he has shewn you.
>
> Let me hope, my dear Sir, that this affair has ceased to give you inquietude, & has not lessened your zeal for Science. Remember you have much cause of comfort & even of exultation. By your great discoveries, mechanical improvements & learned communications, far superior to any that has ever fallen to the lot of one person to make, in your line before you; you have gained a high & universal reputation, as well as the particular esteem & veneration of some of the most respectable persons in the kingdom. This must be most flattering to you, particularly as you must be so conscious of having deserved them, & must, I should think, bear you up against any rubs that fortune never fails to throw in our way, some time or other in our career thro' life....
>
> You must send me a letter in your old style of writing to efface from my mind the mortifying traces of your last...

and if William is financially embarrassed, Watson will happy to send him a couple of hundred pounds.[251]

In later life Caroline was to blame the falling out on the King's *"shabby, mean-spirited advisors* who were undoubtedly consulted on such occasions" (though she explicitly exempts Banks from this charge).[252] Yet the royal wrath must have been impressive indeed if the grant to William of everything he had asked for, and an extra thousand pounds besides, constituted "unworthy treatment". The King was in fact only a year away from his first recorded attack of 'madness' (probably porphyria) and this may perhaps have contributed to the violence of his outburst.[253] On the other hand, the late Roy Porter, an expert on the King's mental health, thought the outburst was in character: the King "certainly was a stubborn, inflexible self-righteous sort, rather insecure, hence unyielding on matters where he thought he was in the right and that he was being taken for a ride".[254] (One might add that the King himself was no model of financial probity: in February 1791 he still owed William for the five 10-ft reflectors he had ordered back in 1783.[255])

Relations between the King and his astronomer would never recover. From now on William's expenditure was monitored with hawk-like intensity. In 1790 he writes a formal letter (probably to Banks):

> Dr. Herschel[256] will prepare without delay an account of the moneys already receiv'd from the King towards the construction of his 40 feet telescope and lay it before Sir Jos: Banks. He has every reason which opinion founded on experience can give, to be certain that the additional money he has ask'd will be sufficient to finish the instrument; nothing but unforeseen accidents can make it otherwise.[257]

Another purpose of the letter, however, is to advise the King that the telescope is up and running, and therefore William would like the annual allowance for expenses to begin:

> As the metal [mirror] is now put in & taken out every night, & the motions work'd to try its figure, & the effect the days polishing has had on it,[258] & as it has already receiv'd one annual polishing, the annual expence of it may fairly be said to have already commenced. Dr. Herschell therefore humbly hopes his Majesty will consent to his annual allowance for expences commencing immediately.

Accompanying the letter is a list of anticipated annual expenses in extraordinary detail. Twelve men engaged in polishing for six weeks are expected to consume one pint of beer per day and this will total £3. 12s. "One man in livery to attend company and strangers that wish to see the telescope in the day time and help to work the instrument during the night", £35. Winter time, "Two fires and four or five candles all night, when the weather is fine. One fire day and night the whole winter. In the day for company that comes to see the telescope, in the night waiting the coming of stars tho' the weather should be cloudy", no actual cost stated but in 1787 he had quoted £15 for this.[259] William is having to account for every last penny.

The time was approaching when the telescope must justify its existence to the republic of letters. The astronomical community waited with bated breath for the revelations that must surely follow its completion (rather as happened with the Hubble Space Telescope in our own day), and no European astronomer would think of visiting England without calling on William at Slough and seeing the giant reflector for himself; Jérôme de Lalande, professor at the Collège Royale in Paris, awaited news of its completion before crossing the Channel expressly for this purpose.[260] But the King had his own, and quite different agenda. He had paid handsomely to have the greatest telescope on earth virtually in his own backyard, he was paying for an astronomer and his assistant and support staff, and he wished visiting royalty and aristocracy to recognize his role as a patron of science. They would be urged to make the short journey from Windsor Castle to Slough, and to admire the great structure with which, as a result of the royal munificence, the King's astronomer could see things hidden from all other observers.

Meanwhile the 40-ft was occupying most of William's daylight hours. The first mirror, cast in October 1785, weighed about 9 cwt, or something under half-a-ton, and had its trial in February 1787. Although, as William later wrote, "its face has been often brought to the highest polish",[261] as already mentioned it proved to be too thin to maintain its shape when tilted in the tube.[262] A year later the second was cast, at twice the weight and of a modified alloy chosen to increase its rigidity. Teams of men polishing manually, and meanwhile "talking and sometimes singing on all sorts of subjects"[263] (unfortunately not recorded for our entertainment), proved unequal to the task, and William developed machinery to do the job (which could if necessary be operated by as few as two men,[264] though a horse was recruited on one occasion[265]). But the second mirror would never attain the "highest polish" of its predecessor, no doubt because of the alloy used; this limitation — which could have reflected badly on his mechanical skills — William kept to himself.

By now the appetite of the scientific community had been whetted for the wonders to come. Long ago, in 1774, Saturn had been the very first object William had 'officially' observed;[266] as it happened, its ring was then edge-on, a configuration that recurs every fifteen years or so. In his early days as a professional astronomer he had examined the planet's five known satellites from time to time,[267] and his interests were no doubt revived in November 1786 by a letter from Lalande that looked forward to the completion of the 40-ft and urged William to study the Saturnian satellites, since it was sixty years since anyone had done this systematically.[268]

The following summer William took up the challenge with the 20-ft reflector, for the planet was now favourably positioned: the ring would soon be edge-on once more. Not only was its glare greatly reduced, but any satellites in the plane of the ring would appear to lie in a straight line. In August and September 1787 he examined the satellites on no fewer than seventeen nights, intrigued by the challenge of making sense of their highly complex ballet around their parent planet. On 19 August he observed them for three hours on end, and thought he had discovered a sixth satellite; but observations in the weeks that followed failed to produce proof of this, partly because of the difficulty he had in distinguishing satellites from background stars.[269]

Next summer he again gave time on the 20-ft to Saturn. But the instrument was currently being used to examine the sky near the zenith, during which time the mirror was horizontal. As a result dew collected on it, and it had tarnished and so became less effective for satellite observations.

By the summer of 1789 the second and more successful mirror for the 40-ft was nearing completion. Saturn's ring was now almost exactly edge-on, and the planet was in rapid retrograde motion, carrying true satellites with it while background stars were left behind. Furthermore, Lalande had just sent new tables of the motions of the five known satellites.[270] William observed the planet on six nights with the 20-ft, and then, on 28 August 1789, he turned the 40-ft towards it. Only four of the five satellites were then visible, but he could see what looked like a sixth. "What makes me take it immediately for a satellite", he noted, "is its exactly ranging with the other four and the ring".[271]

William was under pressure to satisfy the expectations the astronomical community entertained for his new telescope, and the satellite was the answer to his prayers. He dashed off a letter to Banks, asking him to add a brief announcement of its discovery to a paper William already had in press.[272]

On 17 September he was able to go further: "I see six satellites at once, and being perfectly assured that the 2^d is invisible it becomes evident that Saturn has 7 satellites."[273] Euphoric, he wrote again to Banks:

> Perhaps I ought to make an apology for troubling you again with a letter on the same subject as my former one; but if satellites will come in the way of my 40 feet Reflector, it is a little hard to resist discovering them.[274]

With no thought for the problems to be faced by those who arouse expectations they can never hope to satisfy, William prefaced his formal publication of the discoveries with a fanfare proclaiming the arrival of the 40-ft on the astronomical scene:

> But it will be seen presently, from the situation and size of the satellites, that we could hardly expect to discover them till a telescope of the dimensions and aperture of my forty-feet reflector should be constructed; and I need not observe how much we Members of this [Royal] Society must feel ourselves obliged to our Royal Patron, for his encouragement of the sciences, when we perceive that the discovery of these satellites is intirely owing to the liberal support whereby our most benevolent King has enabled his humble astronomer to complete the arduous undertaking of constructing this instrument.[275]

William was careful to understate the role the 20-ft had played, both in discovery (he had suspected the seventh satellite when viewing with the 20-ft on 8 September[276]) and in the elucidation of the periods, so leaving the reader with the impression that the 40-ft had triumphed almost unaided. Not surprisingly, the astronomical community worldwide confidently awaited a succession of such revelations: "We expect daily to partake of new wonders from the Effects of the 40 feet", wrote Banks on 17 November 1789.[277] They waited in vain. Not only that, but the monster had barely reached completion when, in November 1790, William made an observation with the 20-ft that convinced him that true nebulosity did indeed exist and that therefore no telescope could possibly resolve *all* nebulae into stars.[278] The great reflector had now lost what was almost certainly its primary mission.

In the years ahead William did what little he could to fend off the criticisms of colleagues disappointed with the performance of a telescope. It would one day be featured on the Ordnance Survey map, and it was compared in the popular press to the Colossus of Rhodes and the Porcelain Tower of Nankin.[279] Today it is portrayed on the seal of the Royal Astronomical Society. But in astronomy it failed to deliver.

William tried to justify its failure. To examine the whole sky with the 40-ft, he explained in 1799, would take many centuries.[280] Opportunities to use it, he wrote in 1814, were "very scarce", if only because the mirror would be covered with condensation or ice for hours, days or even weeks:[281]

> A 40 feet telescope should only be used for examining objects that other instruments will not reach. To look through one larger than is required is loss of time, which, in a fine night, an astronomer has not to spare; but it ought to be known that the opportunities for using the 40 feet reflector are rendered very scarce by two material circumstances. The first is the changeable temperature of the atmosphere, by which the mirror is often covered by condensation of vapour upon its surface, which renders it useless for many hours; and in cold weather by freezing upon it for the whole night, and even for weeks together; for the ice cannot safely be taken off till a general thaw removes it. The next is that, with all imaginable care, the polish of a mirror exposed like that in the 40 feet telescope, though well covered up, will only preserve its required lustre and delicacy about two years.

The following year, 1815, he published a paper on satellites of Uranus, for he had discovered Oberon and Titania in 1787 and had subsequently convinced himself he had found four more.[282] Not surprisingly, he felt it necessary to explain once again why an observer with the greatest telescope in the world at his disposal was making do with lesser instruments:

> The forty feet telescope having more light than the twenty feet, it ought to be explained why I have not always used it in these observations. Of two reasons that may be assigned, the first relates to the apparatus and the nature of the instrument. The preparations for observing with it take up too much time, which in fine astronomical nights is too precious to be wasted in mechanical arrangements. The temperature of the air for observations that must not be

Pastel portrait of William painted in 1794 by John Russell (1745–1806), a leading portrait painter and pastellist who had a keen interest in science and in scientists. Herschel Family Archives.

On 14 January 1829, John Herschel wrote to Caroline begging her to arrange for him to have "your portrait in oils of the size of my father's" (*Mem*, 234). Caroline complied at once, and on 3 March told John that she felt "much fatigued by sitting eight times within the last ten days to Professor Tielemann for having my picture taken, which he did at my apartment, and now he has taken it home to finish" (*Mem*, 236). The portrait is signed "M. G. Tieleman f[ecit] 1829". There is a short biography of the artist in Bernhard Janssens, *Liersche Kunstschilders uit Vorige Eeuwen 1500–1900* (Lier, 1942). Melchior Gommar [otherwise Maerten Franz or Martin François] Tieleman [or Tielemans or Tielemann] was born in Lier, Belgium, on 8 July 1784. He was a pupil at the Academy of Antwerp, and then in 1805 went to Paris, where he studied with Jacques-Louis David. In 1810 he returned to Belgium to become a drawing teacher in Hasselt. In 1815 Hanover was raised in status to a kingdom, and the following year one of the sons of George III, the Duke of Cambridge, was appointed viceroy; he in turn gave Tieleman the title of court painter, a position that no doubt left Tieleman ample opportunity to pursue private commissions. In 1829 Tieleman returned to his native Lier, where he was appointed director and professor at the Academy, a post he held until shortly before his death on 31 December 1864. Herschel Family Archives.

interrupted, is often too changeable to use an instrument that will not easily accommodate itself to the change: and since this telescope, besides the assistant at the clock and writing desk, requires moreover the attendance of two workmen to execute the necessary movements, it cannot be convenient to have everything prepared for occasional lucid intervals between flying clouds that may chance to occur; whereas in less than ten minutes, the twenty feet telescope may be properly adjusted and directed so as to have the planet in the field of view.[283]

One reason for William's almost-total neglect of the 40-ft lay in the competition it faced, not only from the 20-ft but also from the reflector he completed late in 1799, with the help of his brother Alexander. It was an instrument for his old age, with generous 2-ft mirrors but presenting only a modest challenge to the agility of the observer, being only 10-ft in focal length.

The heroic efforts William made to keep the 40-ft in commission, by regularly repolishing the one-ton mirror, can scarcely have been justified by his pitiful harvest of observations. Each repolishing required him to have the mirror hoisted out of the tube, trundled to the polishing room (which was inconveniently small for so large a mirror[284]), polished for a number of days by a team of labourers recruited for the purpose, trundled back, and re-installed in the tube. Although William was sometimes able to arrange to do this polishing when Bath was out of season and his brother Alexander was free to come and help, it was taxing work for two men approaching old age, and dangerous too. Caroline describes an incident that occurred on 22 September 1807:

> In taking the forty-foot mirror out of the tube, the beam to which the tackle is fixed broke in the middle, but fortunately not before it was nearly lowered into its carriage, &c., &c. Both my brothers had a narrow escape of being crushed to death.[285]

William last observed with the great reflector — though briefly — in August 1814.[286] Caroline notes: "His strength is now, and has for the last two or three years not been equal to the labour required for polishing forty-foot mirrors."[287] If Caroline is correct, his last attempt at polishing had taken place a few weeks before, on 10 June, when she makes a revealing comment:

> My brother, being about this time engaged with re-polishing the forty-foot mirror, it required some time to restore order in his rooms before any strangers could be shown into them, and I again was assisting him to prepare for the reception of the Emperor Alexander and the Duchess of Oldenburg, &c....[288]

Here, and not in the very occasional records of astronomical observations, do we find the motivation for the ceaseless attempts to maintain the mirror of the 40-ft in at least a semblance of good order: the King's astronomer was required to have his great telescope, constructed, staffed and maintained at royal expense, available for royal guests to admire. After all, in his initial application for funds William had described himself as one who "ardently wishes to promote ... the glory of the patron who supports him".

The succession of guests was remorseless. In 1818, three decades after the monster saw first light, and with its constructor in his eightieth year, visitors to William's observatory included: Princess Elizabeth and the Prince of Hesse Homburg with a count and two barons (April); the Prince and Princess Schaumburg von der Lippe (June); the Archduke Michael of Russia "with a numerous attendance" (July); Princess Sophia of Gloucester, the Archbishop of Canterbury and several lords and ladies (August); and the Ertz Herzog Maximilian of Austria (October).[289] Even though the telescope had long been abandoned as an astronomical research tool — if indeed it can be said ever to have had such a function — its role in the entertainment of visitors to the Castle was undiminished, and William had little option but to struggle, year after year, to maintain at least the appearance of an operational instrument. The polishing of the mirror was now beyond him; but as almost nobody was ever allowed actually to look through the telescope (smaller ones were at the disposal of visitors),[290] this was not immediately obvious, and callers could at least marvel at the structure as a whole. And so, in July 1818, when he was in his eightieth year, William attempted once more to restore the mounting; "but the great heat he was exposed to by directing the workmen who are repairing the woodwork, &c., &c., of the 40 ft is surely too much for him".[291] The work continued into August, "but he was all the time too ill".[292] The telescope had become a millstone around William's neck: the story of the 40-ft is a Greek tragedy with *hubris* at its centre.

In the late 1780s, at the height of construction work on the 40-ft, William was directing his army of expensive workmen during the day and doing his best to maintain the programme of sweeps for nebulae at night, and the wonder is that his health stood the strain. When the 40-ft at last came into service in 1789, William was in the second year of his marriage to Mary, and his new-found prosperity allowed him to take proper holidays for the first time in his life. In the years to come the party would include their young son John, born in 1792, and often a niece of Mary's, Sophia Baldwin, went along. Caroline would be left to 'mind the shop'. The trip might last as much as five or six weeks, and William could well have in his pocket as spending-money more than his entire annual pension as Court astronomer.

Yet he continued to make reflectors for sale. Why? Part of the motivation was no doubt vanity, prestige, call it what you will. He rejoiced in his well-deserved reputation "as one of the greatest mechanics of his day", and ambassadors were reduced to writing what were in effect begging letters; for if William declined the commission there was no one else to whom they might turn. The most successful of his great reflectors was the 25-ft he made at the turn of the century for the King of Spain.[293] Its mounting was destroyed in 1808 by Napoleonic troops when they

The very successful 25-ft reflector that William made in 1796/7 for the King of
Spain and shipped to Madrid in 1802, see Bennett, 93–95. The mounting was
destroyed by Napoleonic troops in 1808, but the optics survive in Madrid, as
do the instructions for its assembly. These include this watercolour of the completed instrument. Courtesy of Observatorio Astronomico Nacional, Madrid.

I.

plundered Madrid, but the mirrors (and the immaculate instructions for assembly) survive in Madrid Observatory to this day, and a replica of the instrument has recently been constructed.

But there may well have been another and quite different motivation for William's continued telescope-building. From his amateur days he had been accustomed to being able to see things hidden from all other observers. As early as 1784 Cassini of the Paris Observatory wrote that as no one else had a telescope powerful enough to see the marvels reported by William, "il fallut y croire sur sa parole", "we have to take his word for it".[294] For astronomers this went against the grain. William might be "unser neue Galilei",[295] but Galileo had been careful to solicit confirmation of his observations from other observers. Most of the telescopes William made were for rich and prestigious clients, but some were for fellow astronomers, and he may well have been hoping that they would use the opportunity afforded them to confirm his observational claims.

Some of the trips that William undertook had a practical motive, for they allowed him sight of some of the great industrial processes that were driving Britain's prosperity. The talent that he had demonstrated in the making of large telescopes entitled him to deal on equal terms with leaders of the Industrial Revolution, and he was a welcome visitor to their businesses. What makes William's record of his visits of special interest to the historian of technology is the many careful drawings he made of the machinery shown him and his detailed descriptions.

One trip was unlike any other: his tour of France in 1802 that included an audience with Napoleon himself. William set off on 13 July with Mary, John, and Sophia Baldwin, and arrived in Paris on the 24th, where they stayed the night in a "très mauvais" hotel. During the fortnight that followed they met a succession of distinguished scientists, among them Charles Messier ("Merit is not always rewarded as it ought to be"[296]), and Pierre Simon de Laplace, whose "Lady received company abed, which to those who are not used to it appears very remarkable".[297] On Sunday 8 August the Minister of the Interior conducted William, along with Laplace and the American-born physicist Count Rumford, to Malmaison to meet Napoleon, who received them with great courtesy.

> The first Consul then asked a few questions relating to Astronomy & the construction of the heavens to which I made such answers as seemed to give him great satisfaction. He also addressed himself to M Laplace on the same subject, and held a considerable argument with him in which he differed from that eminent mathematician. The difference was occasioned by an exclamation of the first Consul's, who asked in a tone of exclamation or admiration (when we were speaking of the extent of the sidereal heavens): "And who is the author of all this!" Monsr De la Place wished to shew that a chain of natural causes would account for the construction and preservation of the wonderful system....[298]

In 1797, for reasons unknown, Caroline made the abrupt and inexplicable decision to move out into lodgings. This of course proved hugely inconvenient to her;

and it hampered William's observational work on faint objects, for if he needed Caroline to take notes, her presence must now be planned in advance, and she would afterwards need an escort to see her back to her lodgings.

William frequently returned to investigation of the Sun. It was, he believed, inhabited, and because the stars were other suns they too must be inhabited. To allow him to view the Sun he devised filters of various colours, and as he did so he began to suspect that light and heat from the Sun did not go hand in hand. This led him to experiments with thermometers, and these proved that the Sun radiates heat in regions of the spectrum where it no longer radiates visible light: William had discovered infra-red rays,[299] an achievement that Banks considered outranked everything else he had done, and which Count Rumford thought "the most important since Sr I. Newton's death".[300]

Soon after the abandonment of the programme of sweeps in 1802, William re-examined several of his double stars; and he found that John Michell had been correct: in some of them the two stars had altered position relative to each other in a way that showed that they were companions in space, and presumably in orbit about their common centre of gravity as Newton would have claimed.[301] Michell's argument from probabilities that in many doubles an attractive force (or forces) bound the two stars to each other was now an observational fact. But confirmation that the force was indeed Newtonian gravity would have to wait another generation, and the accumulation of observational data extensive enough to demonstrate that the orbits were Keplerian ellipses.[302]

To the regret and embarrassment of his friends and allies both then and since, William now became obsessed with the study of the coloured effects found in physics and known as 'Newton's rings'. He had many times in life trespassed outside his domain of expertise with great success, but this was a step too far. The Royal Society Committee for Publications allowed his speculations into print only with great reluctance,[303] and when his son John planned a collected edition of his father's papers, he intended to omit those on coloured rings.[304] They are included in the 1912 edition of his collected papers, but only for the sake of completeness.

As he moved into his late seventies, William's health began to worsen. He observed less and less, and his major papers took the form of reflections on the problem of 'the construction of the heavens', where his theory of the gradual evolution of nebulae under the action of gravity and their development into star clusters was illustrated by numerous specimens taken from his catalogues published long before. But these catalogues were organized by class and date of discovery, and this was a format well-nigh useless for the observational astronomer. Nor was this the only major item of unfinished business. His binary stars had been under observation for the better part of four decades, yet it was still not known whether the companions moved around their common centre of gravity in the manner required by Newton's law of gravity. And most important of all, William had seen nothing of the southern skies that to an observer in England were forever below the horizon. His son John must be persuaded to take up astronomy where his

A watercolour of William's 40-ft reflector, in the Herschel Family Archives. It matches exactly the well-known engraving published by William in February 1794, but differs slightly from the illustration published in *Philosophical Transactions* the following year, see Bennett, 90.

father was leaving off.

John had been sent to school at nearby Eton, but after his mother chanced to see him in a fight with an older boy he was taken away and educated privately. At Cambridge he was outstanding in a brilliant year, and after an unsatisfying flirtation with a career in law he was in 1816 elected a Fellow of his Cambridge college, St John's. He was then 24 years of age and on the threshold of what would surely be a distinguished academic career. But William had other plans for him. That summer the family went on holiday to the Devon coast, and there William persuaded John to leave academia and become his apprentice. "I am going", wrote John to a friend, "under my father's directions, to take up the series of his observations where he has left them (for he has now pretty well given over regular observing) and continuing his scrutiny of the heavens with powerful telescopes".[305] The 40-ft was beyond redemption, but it seemed the 20-ft might be restored to health, and so in 1817 two new mirrors were cast for it. John polished one under William's direction, the other he polished himself.

In December 1820 John and his friend James South turned the renovated 20-ft on the Moon and Saturn. But then the structure collapsed. Parts could be salvaged for reuse, but a new (if very similar) 20-ft would have to be built. "I am not sorry for this", John told a friend, "it will afford my poor Father some occupation, which (though able to do very little) he stands much in need of, and is quite a new man when superintending some little repairs, &c."[306] On 1 June 1821 the new instrument was completed, and the time had come for John to make a trial sweep or two. Caroline came out of retirement to act as amanuensis once more, and the 82-year-old William, in what was no doubt a token gesture, helped place the mirror in the tube.[307] The apprentice was now qualified.

The previous year John, South and others had decided to launch what is now the Royal Astronomical Society, believing that the Royal Society could no longer supply the needs of astronomers; but their first nominee for President had been prevailed upon to withdraw by the President of the Royal Society, who feared the competition. The solution was to recruit William, a venerable figure and immune from pressure, on the understanding that his position was purely nominal. Caroline and he assembled a list of double stars as a token contribution to the publications of the infant society.[308]

As the months passed, and William became ever more frail, so worry for the safety of his precious observing records occupied his mind. Caroline had constantly to assure him that they were safe and under lock and key. On 15 August 1822 he was visited by the grandson of the Bulmans with whom he had lodged in Leeds so long ago.[309] Ten days later he was dead.

Anna Christina

Of Anna Christina, the Herschels' fifth child, we know only that she was born on 12 or 13 July 1741, and died of whooping cough on 22 July 1748. Caroline records:

> In 1748, my Parents had to grieve for the loss of a fine Girl who died when 7 years old of the hooping cough, during the time my Mother was confined by the birth of another daughter, who lived only to be 11 month old.[1]

Alexander

Johann Alexander was born on 13 November 1745, fruit of the home leave that his father's regiment had been granted earlier that year. By then Isaac was gone again, and he first saw his infant son when he and his comrades returned to Hanover on 13 February 1746.

Soon Isaac succeeded in obtaining dismission from the army. Work for musicians in Hanover being hard to find, the following winter he moved his family to the neighbourhood of Hamburg, a tedious journey for all concerned as Alexander's bottled milk was frozen and the child was "moaning all the while for his drink".[1] But after a disappointing few months Isaac returned to Hanover and rejoined the Guards, in the hope that the years ahead would be peaceful.

For a time this was so, but in 1756 the Hanoverian Guards were ordered to England. The resulting absence of his father as well as of his two older brothers inevitably disrupted the musical education of the ten-year-old Alexander:

> A great anxiety [writes Caroline] devolved also on my Mother on Alexander's account; he was of an age where he wanted all his Father's attention which had till now been given to his elder brothers. That he would become an excellent musician my Father had no doubt, as he was then already a very good violin player; but he had such an aversion to practicing, looking into a book or improving himself in writing &c which nothing but my Father's mild manner of teaching could have overcome, and unfortunately my Mother's way of treating children was rather severe.[2]

The Guards returned after only a few months away, but on 1 May 1757 they again marched out of Hanover, only to be defeated by the French at Hastenbeck on 26 July. A fortnight later Hanover was occupied by the enemy.

Two years before, Sophia Herschel had married Isaac's fellow-bandsmen, Heinrich Griesbach. Unlike Isaac, Griesbach obtained his dismission soon after Hastenbeck, and in January 1758 he managed to enter occupied Hanover and collect Sophia and their infant son, to settle in nearby Coppenbrügge, where he had been appointed Town Musician. This unlikely development had created an opportunity for Alexander to resume his musical career, for in the absence of his father and brothers he was receiving no instruction whatever. He was only twelve years old and in normal circumstances would have remained two more years in the Garrison School. However, the situation was far from normal, and Isaac reluctantly agreed to his going with Griesbach and Sophia and becoming Griesbach's first apprentice;[3] but on condition that Alexander spend Lent and Advent in Hanover,[4] where Isaac hoped he himself might soon be living as a civilian and so able to help his son with his violin lessons.

Alexander was to reside with Griesbach for six long and unhappy years, for his brother-in-law treated the youth abominably. One suspects he was jealous of the boy's musical talent; but whatever the motivation, every time Alexander's mother had occasion to visit Coppenbrügge, she was appalled at the treatment being meted out to her son

> whom she had seen treated in the most brutal manner by Griesbach: who gave him in her presence without a cause a box on the ear, when the poor boy was sorely afflicted with the Mumps! Nothing but the tears of [Sophia], and the solemn promises of G not to commit such outrage again would have reconciled her to leaving him behind....[5]

Sophia had taken the post of teacher in the local girls' school,[6] and Alexander was much needed as an 'au pair'. He

> was obliged to cleave all the wood for firing, diging in the Garden, &c &c....
>
> His leisure hours were filled up with nursing his little Nephews with whom he stroled in the Vilage, where *Musche* Alexander was not only a favorit with the Landlord of the <u>Celler</u>; but of all the pretty Girls in the Vilage. For the sisters sake he bore all what an illnatured Master could inflict but his spirits were lost, and never perfectly recovered throughout his life.[7]

The memoir written by the eldest of these nephews, George, contains affectionate reminiscences of "Uncle Alexander", who

> took me very frequently in the winter evenings to a neighbour's farmhouse.... Here I used to sit upon one or the other's lap, close round a hot stove — the young men smoking tobacco and the daughters, maids and neighbouring young women assembled with their spinning wheels as busy spinning as possible, while the young men tried to keep pace with their pipes and some one or other telling stories.

Indeed, he believed he owed his life to Alexander:

> I have likewise been once dangerously ill and my Father probably being absent, Uncle Alexander wrapped me up, and with a large cloth fastened me upon his back and carried me to Hanover to a physician, I burning with a violent fever — by which means I was saved.

Early in 1764 — by which time Isaac was back with his family but in declining health — Alexander's apprenticeship came to an end and he returned to Hanover.[8] Unfortunately, the Herschels were living in cramped quarters, and so it was arranged for Alexander to board with the City Musician. He

> had little else to do but to give a dayly Lesson to an Apprentis and to blow an Coral from the Markt Turm; so that nearly all his time could be given to Practice....[9]

Then, in the winter of 1765/6, Alexander secured the post of first oboist in the regimental band of Prince Charles, brother to Queen Charlotte and a pupil of Jacob Herschel's. Alexander would thus be well placed to secure one of the coveted vacancies in the Court Orchestra, for "Prins Carl being at Hannover, it was known that all vacancies would be filled with men from his favorit Band".[10] Unfortunately, when the vacancy occurred Alexander was one of two equally favoured candidates, and both had to agree to work for half-salary. "This my Father foresaw would involve us in great difficulty, for he had early discovered (and not been sparing in admonishing) that Alex. was no economist and addicted to expensive pleasures."[11]

In 1767 Isaac at last succumbed to the ill-health that had plagued him since Dettingen. Jacob, the new head of the family, and his widowed mother now had to face life without Isaac. "About Alexander we had no fear that he would by practising a strict economy, and attending some of his late Father's Scholars, and others, do well enough till by an increase in salary his situation would become more easy."[12] Their brother William was by now established in his adopted homeland of England, and resided in Bath, where there were rich pickings for enterprising musicians. Jacob soon went to pay him an extended visit, and this left Alexander unsupervised:

> I was extremely discomposed [writes Caroline] at seeing Alex, associating with young men who led him into all manner of expensive pleasures, which involved him in debts for the hire of Horses, and Carioles &c. and I was (though he knew my inability of helping him) made a partaker in his fears that these scrapes should come to the knowledge of our Mother.[13]

It was at this stage that Alexander began to display hints of the exceptional mechanical talent that he shared with William. Caroline records:

> My Mother Span, I was at work on a set of ruffles of dresden work for my brother Jacob, and Alex oftens sat by us and amused us and himself with making all sorts of things in pasteboard, or contriving to make a 12 hours Kuku Clock go a Week.[14]

Jacob returned in July 1769 well pleased with his time in Bath, and a year later he was off again, this time with Alexander, who had been given two years' leave of absence from the Court Orchestra. Alexander was to stay in Bath not two, but forty-six years. He quickly became a member of the band at the Orchard Street Theatre, and performed there for most of his long residence in the town. Like his three brothers, Alexander had the ability to play any instrument he laid his hands on: a violinist and oboist in Hanover, in Bath he was known first as a clarinetist,[15] and then as a cellist whose solos Caroline declares were "divine".[16] An obituary notice in a Bristol paper would describe him as "the admiration of the frequenters of concerts and theatres of both [Bath and Bristol], as principal violoncello".[17] He took pupils,[18] but he was especially esteemed as the accompanist of vocalists, even though he had strong views about keeping strict time and sought to impose these on his fellow-performer.[19] He was equally strict with his own attendance:

when in 1816 injury at last forced his retirement to Hanover, the *Bath Chronicle* announced

> the intention of the musical professors of Bath to pay a gratuitous tribute to the talents, character, age and virtues of Mr Herschell of this city who has been their co-adjudicator in the orchestra, on the Violincello, for the last 45 years, during which period he has but once, and then through indisposition, absented himself from his professional duties, till the late severe accident he met with and from which he is now but slowly recovering.[20]

With all the coming and going between Hanover and Bath, William was kept well informed about the plight of his little sister Caroline, whom their mother saw as a permanent source of cheap help in the family home; and in August 1772 he descended upon Hanover in person, and carried Caroline off to Bath. He and Alexander would pay for substitute help in the house.[21]

In Bath Caroline found herself sharing the attic floor of their home with Alexander. Caroline had arrived at the start of the winter season, and she fully understood that William was heavily committed. Sometimes Alexander was able to spend time with her, but

> it did me no good, for he never was of a cheerful disposition, but always looking on the dark side of everything, and I was much disheartened by his declaring it to be impossible for my Brother to teach me anything which would answer any purpose but that of making me miserable.[22]

It seems that Alexander was prone to depression, for in her old age Caroline would write to her niece Margaret: "I do not wish to write in what my dear brother William used to call a Dick Doleful style, when our brother Alexander was in the dismals, and out of which we often succeeded in laughing him".[23] His reputation as handed down in the family was to be that of "a most simple minded creature, with a warm heart, but a contracted mind, and very taciturn".[24] Taciturnity was the last thing Caroline wanted in one of the only two people around her who spoke German.

With the end of the season she expected William to give her systematic instruction in singing. Instead, to her indignation, she found the household being turned into a telescope manufactory, with

> Alex putting up a huge turning machine (which in the Autham [autumn] he brought with him from Bristol where he used to spend the summer) in a Bedroom for turning patterns, grinding glasses & turning eye-pieces &c.[25]

Very surprisingly, both of the musician-brothers possessed a quite exceptional talent for things mechanical. William's practical abilities quickly made themselves known to the outside world as a result of his manufacture of telescopes for his own use and for sale. Much less familiar is the selfless role that Alexander played over the years in this construction work — though from time to time he allowed himself a distraction or two:

I was in making [writes Caroline in 1773] a Tube for a 15 feet refracting Tele-scope of pastebord sometimes assisted by my brother Alexander; but this could happen but seldom because he had a Bride — the eldest of two Sisters (Friend of Mrs Bulman and Neighbours) but their habits and pursuits being intirely different from mine I never became more than distantly acquainted with them.... [*Footnote:* Alexander soon after felt very unhappy on having seen Miss Cohlman one evening walking and talking very familiarly with a former suspected lover, and He was not happy, till His Brother persuaded the Lady to return the Ring by which they were Betrothed.][26]

In 1774 William moved out of the centre of town to a house near Walcot Parade, next to a builder's yard where there were labourers available when required. But the house was so small that "my Brother Alexander was obliged on the return from his Somer engagement to take Lodgings in Town, but came dayly to spend his leisure hours with us, or in the workshop".[27] He

frequently partuck in the laborious and Mechanical contrivances and where strength and courage was requiered he was always foremost to lend his assist-ance, and even yet I shuder on recollecting the dangerous situation he was in when the Gages of the 20 feet Mirror were struck standing at the top of the hous supporting himself with his left arm at a Chimne-stack whilst with his right at full strech he was guiding the Plumb line.[28]

The distractions however continued:

In this manner best part of the Sumer spent without any change, but when our Landlady with her Step-Daughter came to take Tea with us. Miss Whiler was a very handsom Girl, and looked upon as the Bride of Alexander; but it was soon found that she had more than one favoured Lover; and poor Alex was jilted again; and went soon after to forget his disappointmen in business to where he was engaged for the rest of Sumer.[29]

At this period William and Alexander were both busy musicians with their liveli-hoods to earn. The elder was obsessed with astronomy as a hobby, the younger found pleasure in helping him with the practical challenges that arose as a result. But Alexander had to give priority to music: "My Brother Alex. was absent from Bath for some months every Sumer; but when at home he took much pleasure to execute some turning or Clockmakers work for his Brother."[30] Even so, he did not always reach the standard of dedication that Caroline looked for: "Alexander was always very alert and assisting when anything new was going forward, but he wanted perseverance and never liked to confine himself at home for many hours together."[31]

Alexander showed himself at his best when Dietrich astonished his family by fleeing Hanover in the summer of 1777, with the intention of sailing for the East Indies. William set out from Bath to head him off, and while he was away word reached Caroline that Dietrich was lying ill in London:

> Alex was engaged at Bristol but used to walk over to see me on Sundays. I went to meet him, and he no sooner saw the letter than we hastened home and whilst taking a hasty breakfast, post horses were ordered; and he was with D. next morning and had him removed to a Lodging, where Dr Smith and a fourthnights nursing brought him so far that by easy stages he could be removed to Bath. Poor Alex. was rejoysing at having saved the life of a brother though it was at the loss of his business with all his stock of Cash; for, poor fellow was never famous for being an oeconomist; especially where he thought he could assist a fellow creature in want.[32]

William was meanwhile cherishing hopes that Alexander would share his enthusiasm for observing the night sky. In his "Experiments on the construction of specula" for 2 April 1779, he records: "I began to repolish a Gregorian speculum belonging to my brother Alex's telescope",[33] and three years later he speaks of "Alexander's new speculum".[34] In May 1782 William gave a fellow-guest at supper the impression that "His sister and his brother ... were as fond of astronomy as himself and all used to sit up, star-gazing, in the coldest frosty nights",[35] and it is possible that this was true of Alexander, though not of Caroline at this stage in her life. Certainly Alexander would one day retire to Hanover taking with him a 5-ft Gregorian with 9-inch mirrors, a sizeable instrument.[36]

It was in March 1781 that William came across what proved to be the planet Uranus, and in the aftermath of this discovery King George III conferred on him a pension, his only duties as astronomer being to reside near Windsor and be available to royal guests when required.[37] A year later the King himself placed an order for five 10-ft reflectors, a clear signal that William was welcome to use the daylight hours to supplement his salary, by making telescopes for sale.

This had important consequences for Alexander. His brother was now making reflectors, not to pursue a hobby that was a drain on his purse, but as part of a flourishing commercial business. Alexander therefore need no longer eke out his winter income by undertaking musical engagements out of season;[38] instead, he could spend his summers with William as part of the production team, and there can be little doubt that he shared in the financial rewards.

Alexander had accompanied William and Caroline in their move from Bath to their new home at Datchet, and he then spent two whole months with them helping to get the semi-derelict property into some sort of order, before returning to Bath. There he continued to occupy the house at 19 New King Street where William and Caroline had lived, and in whose basement the two brothers had unsuccessfully attempted in 1781 to cast a mirror 3-ft in diameter. After a few weeks in Datchet William returned there to gather up fragments of the mirror for future use, and the brothers took the opportunity to cast a new 12-inch mirror for what was then William's major telescope, the 'small' 20-ft.

The problem of Alexander's love life remained unresolved. His siblings had no confidence in his ability to handle sensibly matters of the heart, now that he was on his own. Jacob and Dietrich in Hanover, and William and Caroline in Datchet, were equally exercised. Alexander had originally come to England with leave of absence from the Court Orchestra, but with his decision to remain in England his post had been filled. As it happened, the recent death of one of the members of the Orchestra had created a vacancy, and so no sooner had word of William's appointment at Windsor reached Hanover than Dietrich wrote to him saying:

> ... we want to know what poor Alex is doing alone at Bath. We have some prospect of getting him into the Orchestra here with a salary of 200 thalers through the Chamberlain. It that succeeds he could probably earn 50 or 100 more for himself and then he could live comfortably. But if this fails positively you should get him [omission]. He cannot possibly be happy at Bath alone. I should like nothing better than to have him and I am sure he would not miss anything here so alone as he is. Old Beneke is dead; that is another place vacant.

Presumably Alexander indicated interest in the suggestion, for at the end of the year Jacob wrote from Hanover to tell William that he had persuaded the Chamberlain there to open negotations with Alexander on the basis of an initial salary of 200 thalers. Jacob had described his brother as a good soloist and accompanist, but had stopped short of claiming he was a virtuoso. If the salary was acceptable, Jacob hoped an audition with the King in person might be arranged, unusual though this would be.[39]

Meanwhile, William and Caroline had been urging Alexander to seek work in London "where he had the offer of the most profitable engagements and we should then have had him near us".[40] London their brother found unappealing, but a letter (in German) from Jacob to William written in May 1783 shows that negotiations with Hanover were still continuing: "Alexander's business rests now with the Chamberlain, who unfortunately is very careless about orchestral matters."[41] By now, however, Alexander was developing a more compelling reason for remaining in Bath, for the register of the church in the Bath suburb of Walcot tells us that he married a widow, Margaret Smith of Bath, on 31 July 1783.[42] Caroline comments on Alexander's return to Bath from Datchet in the autumn of 1782: "... before we saw him again the next year he was married (wretchedly) and we saw him never otherwise but discontented after this our separation."[43]

During their first year in Datchet William constructed a second 20-ft reflector, known as the 'large' because of its 18-inch mirrors, and Caroline records that William tried to get some aspects of the machinery done in London, but that the professionals there could not match Alexander for workmanship: "But all what was done in Town seldom answered expectation, and was reserved to be executed with improvements by Alex. during the few months he spent with us."[44] The reflector's bell-mechanism may well be one example of this. The 20-ft came into service in October 1783, and by the end of the year William and Caroline were collaborating in sweeps for nebulae. The instrument had a field of view of only 15′,[45] but there was time as the sky slowly rotated overhead for William to examine a much wider strip. To take advantage of this, a workman slowly raised and lowered the tube in an oscillatory motion. It was important for the workman to know when to stop and reverse the direction of movement, and for this William in 1784 introduced a machine that rang a bell at the extremities of the sweep.[46] Evidently the mechanism was not completely satisfactory, for a year later William asked Alexander to devise something better.

His brother's initial response is contained in two letters still extant, the first dated 9 May 1785 and the second written a few weeks later.[47] These documents are in the National Maritime Museum in Greenwich, as is the mechanism from the later 20-ft that William's son John was to make in close imitation of his father's instrument and which incorporated parts from it. John's mechanism may well have originated in Alexander's mechanism for William's 20-ft.

While in Bath, William had purchased a timepiece from the noted maker Thomas Field,[48] but evidently Alexander also made him a clock, for in his notes for 26 September 1783 William writes: "Fields [time]piece has gained 7″ upon Alexander's. I set them together last night at this time."[49] William's need for a reliable clock was solved the following October when Alexander Aubert presented him with a regulator by Shelton.[50] But all three clocks continued in use, for on 30 July 1786 Caroline "wound up the Sid[ereal] Time piece, Field's and Alex. Clocks".[51] After William's marriage in 1788 Alexander's clock was, it seems, assigned to her for use in her sweeps for comets, for her observing books repeatedly cite the time by "Alexander's Clock", and a note of the correction required to make Alexander's time conform to that of the Shelton.[52]

It seems therefore that Alexander succeeding in making a clock comparable to that by Field, though not of course to Shelton's. We have an account of it in the anecdotes recorded in 1833 by James Stewart:

> There stands a clock in [John] H[erschel]'s Laboratory, which bears the inscription "Alex^r Herschel fecit". He was a brother of Sir William's, and had a strong mechanical genius though he only indulged it for the sake of amusement. This clock can go very well and as an amateur performance is rather extraordinary.[53]

At some stage, and most probably in the late 1780s or early '90s,[54] Alexander made a much simpler 'journeyman' clock for Caroline,[55] one that she could take outdoors and which loudly ticked the seconds. It became known in the family as "the monkey-clock",[56] and its function was to enable her to correlate the time of an observation made in the open air with the accurate time as shown a few seconds later on the clock inside the house.[57] The monkey-clock was also used by William when he wished to polish a mirror in a given manner for a specified number of seconds or minutes. Caroline speaks of it in a letter she wrote to John on 5 December 1826:

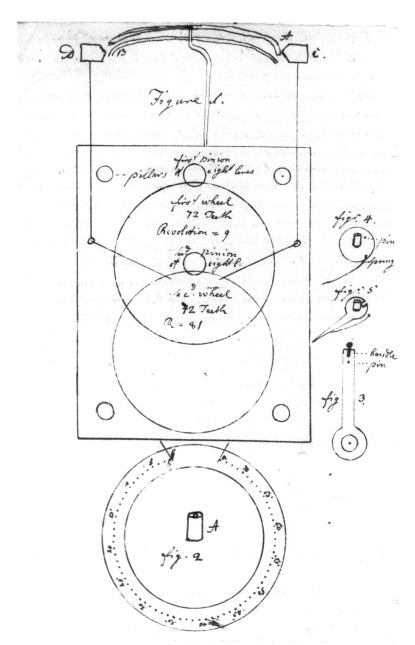

Even when he was in Bath and so at a distance from Slough, Alexander contributed to the development of William's major telescopes. In this diagram, sent with an explanatory letter on 9 May 1785, Alexander sketches the bell mechanism he has devised for the 'large' 20-ft. Courtesy of the National Maritime Museum.

Bell machine used by John Herschel, and probably based on that made by Alexander for William's 20-ft reflector. Courtesy of the National Maritime Museum.

You mention a monkey-clock, or jack, in your paper I would only notice (if you mean the jack in the painted deal case) that Alex made it merely to take with me on the roof when I was sweeping for comets, that I might count seconds by it going softly downstairs till I was within hearing of the beat of the timepiece on the first floor (at that time our observatory) all doors being open. Your father never used it except when polishing the forty-foot....[58]

On retirement Alexander was to take his clockmaker's tools with him to Hanover, where they were sold for scrap after his death.[59]

In the spring of 1785, when the Bath season was drawing to a close, William wrote to Alexander to invite him to resume what was evidently a well-established partnership in the construction of telescopes:

I wish very much the time may come when your Bath business will be over that we may see you and my good Sister[-in-law] here at Datchet again. I have a great deal of work upon my hands. I have bought a complete set of tools for working in Brass; erected a small forge; have a Brass workman; the Cabinet maker is employed; the Joiner at work; the Smith forging away, so that I hope to get some instruments finished pretty fast. My <u>Brass Man</u> (as we call him) is a stupid fellow, but knows a good deal of the business. When you come he shall be your journey-Man [semi-skilled assistant]. He admires your workmanship much, what I have shewn him of it.[60]

Caroline says of the construction of the 'large' 20-ft, that "during the 3 or 4 months Alex. could be absent from Bath, the mirrors and optical parts were nearly completed".[61] But this cannot be right.[62] Perhaps she is thinking of the 40-ft, for whose construction William successfully requested funds from the King in August 1785.[63] Thereafter this huge undertaking dominated his life and that of his sister, and — out of season — his brother.

Alexander was spending his summers with William,[64] and evidently his wife came too, to tax Caroline's patience. William's granddaughter writes that the brothers

continued to do all the delicate work for the telescopes themselves. Alexander, being especially expert in brass work, probably undertook all the turning of eye-pieces, screws, &c on the lathe which they had brought from Bath.... William attended to the shaping and polishing of the mirrors.[65]

Alexander's expertise in eyepieces had already allowed him to repair the 7-ft reflector William had made for his Bath friend and ally, Dr William Watson. Watson wrote on 23 November 1783:

Your brother is so kind as to undertake my Telescope, & finds the adjustment is right except that the peice of turned cocoa [of the eyepiece], wch is glued into the slider, & into wch the comunication-peices screw, is awry.

One of the earliest Continental astronomers to contact William for help with instrumentation had been Johann Hieronymous Schröter, chief magistrate of Lilienthal, near Hanover, and the only one of William's contemporaries to rival his ambitions in astronomy. Schröter wrote to William on 2 February 1783, introduced himself by citing his acquaintance with Jacob and Dietrich Herschel, and asked if William knew the name of a London instrument maker who might replace the broken mirror of his 4½-ft reflector, money no object. Evidently William agreed to make the mirror himself, for later in the month Schröter sent the exact dimensions and ordered a small mirror to go with it. William did not get around to supplying the mirrors until the end of the year, but Schröter had the necessary patience, and on 14 January he wrote to express his delight with the result and to say the instrument was being assembled in Hanover. Could William now supply him with eyepieces?

On 17 July Schröter wrote again, this time to confirm his order for a 7-ft telescope that William had offered to arrange to have made for only 22 guineas by "une personne à qui j'ai enseigné de faire des miroirs" — in fact, Alexander. A full year later Schröter was still awaiting delivery, but on 29 August 1785 he wrote to ask if William's brother could also make him a 4-ft reflector. Soon after he wrote again to say that a Herr von Moll also wished to have mirrors for a 4-ft.[66]

Meanwhile other enquiries had reached William from Germany. On 20 July 1785 he wrote to the distinguished astronomer Johann Elert Bode, "You asked by way of Monsieur Zach, if I could furnish Newtonian telescopes for amateurs and what the prices would be. My brother makes them of every size".[67] A year later Watson wrote to enquire after William's "design of setting up your brother to make [reflectors] for sale" (but, unfortunately, we lack William's reply). More significantly, in 1787 the Italian astronomer Barnaba Oriani recorded in his diary during a visit to Slough, that "his brother [Alexander] makes telescopes for sale when not engaged as a musician in Bath".[68]

No surviving reflector has been identified as having been made by Alexander at Bath, and there is no evidence that William made further attempts to set his brother up in business. On the other hand, the plain statement by Oriani, three years after Alexander's first commission, is hard to ignore. But (as we shall see) Alexander was then soon to become a widower, after which he would have neither family nor musical commitments in Bath out of season, and so be free to get on the London coach and alight at Slough whenever he was so minded. Furthermore, at some time before his bereavement he moved out of 19 New King Street,[69] and he then no longer had a foundry in his home. It seems very likely, therefore, that from this time on he devoted his mechanical skills to helping with the construction work at Slough. This is confirmed by the "Anecdotes" retold in 1833 by William's son John and recorded by James Stewart, brother to John's wife Margaret:

> ... this eccentric man ... lived at Bath long after D[r] [William] H[erschel] had moved to Datchet; he was a musician by profession, but all his thoughts sleeping or waking were directed to the subject of mechanics. He never moved away from his own home, except to pay a yearly visit to his brother's family, and then invariably came accompanied by his turning-lathe and other implements, and getting himself & them established the moment of his arrival, in the workshop (now H's observatory) scarcely left that apartment during the whole period of his stay. His appearance at meals with the family was never thought of — and he was indulged by them in his humour to his heart's content — allowed to pass his time in his own way & never asked one question or interrupted in his pursuits by any thing. He used to go away after his week of visitation had expired, having scarcely seen his friends all the time, but declaring himself quite delighted with their society.[70]

In the summer of 1786 the King instructed William to go to Göttingen to present the university with one of the 10-ft reflectors he had ordered. Alexander agreed to go with him — they would have an opportunity to visit their relatives in Hanover[71] — and the two brothers were away for nearly two months. "Alexander longs to come home as much as I do", William wrote to Caroline, "that we may go on with the great work [the 40-ft]; otherwise this is a very pleasant place tho' I would not wish to spend much time here [Hanover]. The 40 feet I hope is not hurt by any accident or otherwise polishing the speculum will be the first work we undertake".[72] Meanwhile Caroline tolerated Alexander's wife as best she could.[73]

The following summer, however, Alexander for once found himself unable to help — he could manage only a fleeting visit, to greet Jacob who was over from Hanover. His wife was now seriously ill, too ill to be left for long. She died that winter, on or about 5 February 1788.[74]

Some three months later, on 8 May, William married his widowed neighbour Mary Pitt, with Alexander and Caroline as witnesses. Caroline, who no longer took first place in her brother's affections, was later to destroy her records of the ensuing decade,[75] and as a result we are ill-informed about the weeks or months that Alexander no doubt continued to spend each summer with his brother. Certainly he was with them on 9 September 1788, when "My Brother Alexander saw the five Satellites" of Saturn.[76] It is probable that on one or other of these visits Alexander helped design and construct two mechanisms for the 40-ft that are today in the National Maritime Museum. One is the bell mechanism to indicate the limits of the oscillations. The other served a quite different purpose. In both the 20- and the 40-ft the observer's viewing gallery had to be raised or lowered to conform with the altitude of the tube, and to move that of the 40-ft required the services of two workman, one to each side. It was essential that they work in unison if the gallery was not to tilt, and for this two bell-mechanisms were provided, whose signals would enable the men to keep pace with each other. The Greenwich mechanism is one of these.[77]

When Caroline's records resume, we find that Alexander was spending annually anything up to three summer months at Slough. Every single year, with the possible exception of 1814, Alexander arrived ready and eager to help, whether William himself was present, or absent on one of his many holidays. Thus in 1801 Alexander reached Slough on 1 July, and on 25 August William — then on a trip that took him to Wales — wrote to Caroline:

> Tell my good brother that I long to be at work again with my telescopes, and that one of the first things to be done will be to repolish to 40 feet speculum. Then I shall also polish myself a beautiful 10 feet. The 5 feet will also be completely put right....
>
> I hope they will not want Alexander at Bath this good while, as I shall have much occasion for his help in fitting up 3 seven feet telescopes. Let William [a servant] when he goes to Windsor call on Taylor the cabinet maker, to inquire if the tube and two stands are finished.
>
> I am glad to hear that our brother has cleaned the time piece. If he finds it

Alexander's bell mechanism to indicate the limits of the oscillations of William's 40-ft reflector. Courtesy of the National Maritime Museum.

lose or gain, by the transit of the stars, I wish he would regulate it accordingly as near as he can; and if he will be so good as to write down how many divisions he moves the adjustment we shall know how to regulate for the future.

If the regular time of winding up has been changed by the cleaning please to wind it up again by the marks I mentioned in my last, next Sunday morning. Has Alexander had time to clean the clock in the 40 feet; for that I suppose must be full of dust?[78]

The 40-ft was now a millstone around William's neck:[79] even to keep the one-ton mirror in something resembling working order was an arduous burden as its creator moved into later life. Alexander's visits continued, and Caroline says on occasion that this was specifically to help with maintaining the 40-ft. Hoisting the massive mirror out of the tube for repolishing was a hazardous operation. Thus on 22 September 1807:

In taking the forty-foot mirror out of the tube, the beam to which the tackle is fixed broke in the middle, but fortunately not before it was nearly lowered

The one surviving 'handle bell' from William's 40-ft reflector. Courtesy of the National Maritime Museum.

into its carriage, &c., &c. Both my brothers had a narrow escape of being crushed to death.[80]

Nor was this the only such occasion. "I long to hear that the forty-foot instrument is safely got down", Caroline wrote to William's son John in 1823. "[Y]our father, and Uncle A. too, have had many hair-breadth escapes from being crushed by the taking in and out of the mirror."[81]

On 29 June 1815 "Alex came to assist his brother",[82] and he stayed until 11 August. Alexander was now approaching seventy, and this was to be his last of his many visits. On 4 February 1816 a letter arrived at Slough with news that he had sustained a serious injury to his knee. Two days later he wrote to reassure Caroline:

I will only say that Mr Edwards assured me this morning that everything goes on well, more so than could be expected. Today makes seven days and seven nights that my leg has laid in one position; at first he told me it would require a month or more time but today he gives me hopes that in another week I should sitt upon a proper chair in the daytime.[83]

But later in the month his condition had deteriorated: "I could not breath and for three hours I expected every moment to be my last."[84] Caroline offered to come and nurse her widower brother; but by the time her letter arrived he felt well enough to decline.[85]

It then emerged that the accident had happened at a particularly inauspicious time for him. Alexander had then been fortunate enough to have an unusually high number of pupils, and although Caroline later wrote that "Poor brother Alexander [was] on the brink of being ruined by mercenaries who took advantage of his growing infirmities",[86] he had entertained hopes that by summer he would have been able to clear his debts. Now that he was no longer mobile, these hopes were dashed.[87]

Bath no longer held its attraction for him, and in the summer it was agreed that the time had come for him to return to his native Hanover, to be with his youngest brother Dietrich and his wife. On 31 July Alexander left Bath for Slough where he stayed a month, after which, on 2 September, Caroline saw him safely on board the boat that would take him to Bremen.[88] The repatriation proved a success, and Alexander "was by the assistance of his Brother W^m enabled to retire for the remainder of his life as an independent private Gentleman".[89] He lived happily in Hanover until his death, on 15 March 1821 at the age of seventy-five.[90] He was buried near his parents, at the Gartenfriedhof.[91]

William sent Dietrich £50 to cover any funeral expenses, and some of the money went towards a grave-stone.[92] Caroline, it seems, later regretted that she and William had not made a retirement home for Alexander in Slough: "Alex was a good creature and I lament we had not a little longer pations [patience], he was too good to come here [Hanover]!"[93]

Sadly, no representation of Alexander is known to have survived. Soon after her return to Hanover after William's death in 1822, Caroline found a silhouette or "shade" of Alexander which she sent to John for his mother to have,[94] but if this still exists its whereabouts are unknown.

Maria Dorethea

Maria Dorethea, the Herschels' seventh child, was born on 8 June 1748, and died from an unrecorded cause on 21 April 1749.[1]

Caroline*

"... a poor solitary old maid, like myself."[1]

1750–1759: A CHILD IN THE SHADOW OF WAR

Throughout her long life, Carolina Lucretia, the youngest of Isaac and Anna's four daughters, thought of bottles as half-empty rather than half-full. Her troubled childhood shaped her sombre outlook.

She was born on 16 March 1750, during one of the few periods of contentment in her parents' married life. Although Isaac was in poor health as a result of the hardships he had experienced in military campaigns, Hanover was at peace. He and Jacob could carry out their duties as bandsmen from the comfort of their home, and of an evening Isaac would encourage his sons to practise music, and to learn to think.

Then, when Caroline was four years old, smallpox struck the family. Her younger brother Frantz Johann died of the disease, and although Caroline survived, "I did not escape being totally disfigured and suffering some injury to my left eye".[2] She grew up to be well under five feet tall;[3] and her loving but realistic father was to warn her

> against all thoughts of marrying, saying as I was neither hansom nor rich, it was not likely that anyone would make me an offer, till perhaps, when far advanced in life, some old man might take me for my good qualities.[4]

Isaac was overly-optimistic: Caroline was to die an old maid.

Soon war clouds began to gather, and when Caroline was barely six, her little world fell apart. The number of military bandsmen in the family had increased to four, with the enlistment of William and the marriage of Sophia to Heinrich Griesbach; and in the winter of 1755/6, when the Hanoverian Guards were summoned to reinforce England against a possible invasion from France, all four men of the family marched out of Hanover, leaving Caroline and her mother in tears.

> I found myself now with my Mother alone in a room all in confusion, in one corner of which my little brother Dietrich lay in his cradle; my tears flowed like my Mother's but neither of us could speak. I snatch't a large handkerchief of my Father's from a chair and took a stool to place it at my Mother's feet,

---

* In her old age, Caroline wrote two autobiographies, and these are to be found in *CHA*. Her life-story, with special reference to her relationship with William, is told in detail in *P'ship*. The present biographical sketch therefore does not aspire to completeness, but focuses on how her personality was formed and how it influenced her later actions and her thinking.

on which I sat down, and put into her hands one corner of the handkerchief, reserving the opposite one for myself; this little action actually drew a momentary smile into her face. I could go on describing what passed every succeeding hour throughout that day, but one word will serve for a thousand, which is, we were completely wretched.[5]

Writing in extreme old age of the four years that followed, she repeated: "I can only say that I was completely wretched ... there was no one who cared anything about me."[6] She had in fact written "cared *much* about me"; but on second thoughts she substituted the still more bleak "anything". For love, she of course looked to her parents, and to William, the only one of her brothers to show her affection. But for most of her formative years her ailing father was absent with the regiment; and in 1757 William fled to England as a refugee, and chose to settle in his adopted country. Her mother, we note, is among those whom she remembered as caring nothing about her.

1759–1772: GLOOMY PROSPECTS

Because she was a girl, Caroline was not taught arithmetic in the Garrison School,[7] and when she went to England as a young adult to become William's housekeeper, she could barely add 2 and 2. He would have to teach her what she needed to keep track of the household monies, and later in life she would always carry the multiplication tables around with her.[8] When she left school at fourteen, her loving father — the one person in her life who never failed her, and whose almanac would one day be placed in her coffin[9] —

... wished to give me something like a polished education; but my Mother was particularly bent upon it, it should be rough; but at the same time a useful one.[10]

Unfortunately for Caroline, she was in effect an only daughter. Sophia had been allowed instruction in needlework and this had enabled her to leave home and go into service, and before Caroline was five Sophia had married and soon had a family of her own. The next two girls, Anna Christina and Maria Dorethea, were already in their graves when Caroline was born. Caroline therefore represented her illiterate mother's sole prospect of lifelong help around the house. Anna regretted the education her husband was giving to their sons, which encouraged them in ambitions above their station;[11] and she was determined to do what she could to prevent her one remaining daughter from ever quitting the family home.

On occasion in later life, Caroline managed to overcome her abiding sense of resentment long enough to see her mother's point of view:

I have often felt myself exceedingly at a loss for the want of those few accomplishments of which I was thus by an erroneous though well meant opinion of my Mother's deprived....[12]

But such occasions were rare, and for most of the time she sought to banish Anna from her memory. In 1825 Caroline was to purchase the plot where her mother and father were buried, and over it she had built what she describes as "a vault" in which she too was to be interred.[13] She paid for a stone for herself,[14] and later, when she was in her mid-nineties, she composed for it first one inscription,[15] and then a second; and it is a German translation of this second inscription that can be seen on her tomb today.[16] In both of them her father's presence in the same place is commemorated; in neither is her mother so much as mentioned. Caroline treasured the memory of her father, but she sought to eliminate her mother from the record, denying her even a name on the stone over her grave.

From her earliest years Anna had inculcated Caroline with the Protestant work-ethic. When school ended in mid-afternoon, Caroline had gone on to classes in knitting for another three hours; so tiny was she that when making stockings for Alexander she had had to stand upright, and even so the work touched the floor.[17] When she was eight, and in the immediate aftermath of the French occupation, she had done her best to help her mother earn some extra money by working on the tents and linen required by the troops.[18] But as Caroline approached adolescence the prospects of her earning a living outside the Herschel home were bleak. One possible career for a working-class girl was that of governess, looking after the children of a well-to-do family. But governesses were usually expected to teach French to their charges and to have other genteel accomplishments, and Anna did her best to prevent her daughter from qualifying for such a post:

> My Mother would not consent to my being taught french, and my brother Dietrich was even denied a dancing master because she would not permit my learning along with him though the entrance had been paid for us both; so all my Father could do for me was to indulge me (and pleas himself) sometimes with a short lesson on the Violin; when my Mother was either in good humour or out of the way.[19]

Understandably, Caroline was to look back with regret on these missed opportunities, remembering "the disagreeable feeling of dependence to which [Isaac's] younger children for many years were doomed", a taste of "the mortifications and disappointments which have attended me throughout a long life".[20]

Jacob, who had accompanied William in his flight from war-torn Hanover, returned from England in 1759 to take up a post in the Court Orchestra. But this created its own problems: Jacob saw himself as entitled to be waited on hand and foot, "and poor I got many a wipping for being too awkward at supplying the place of footman or waiter".[21] He would descend on the family when he required feeding,

> ... but it generally happened that before he departed his Mother was as much out of humour with him as he was at the beefsteaks being hard, and that I did not know how to clean knives and forks with brickdust.[22]

Caroline's beloved father was at last reunited with his family in May 1760, but his daughter's joy was dampened by the realization that his health was poor and ever-deteriorating. In August 1764 he suffered a stroke,[23] and although he made a limited recovery, the family became increasingly dependent upon the money brought in by Jacob.

Meanwhile, in March 1764, Caroline had reached the age of fourteen, time to leave school fortified by the rite of passage, Confirmation, by which her mother set such store. By ill-luck the ceremony coincided with a long-awaited visit from the best-loved of her siblings, her brother William. On 2 April 1764, the day after Isaac had helped his children to view an eclipse of the Sun seen reflected in a tub of water,[24] William's arrival was marked by "a continual tumult of joy".[25] He was to be in Hanover for no more than a fortnight, but the heartless Anna ensured that Caroline was "almost intirely absent from the groope, either to fetch and carry something, or attend at school and church".[26] Her daughter never forgot the morning when the coach carried her brother away to his distant home in a foreign land, passing the church door at the very moment when she was to receive her first Communion: "I was nearly annih[i]lated by the Postilion's blast he gave in his horn."[27]

Now that Caroline had left school, Anna was able to turn her into a full-time household drudge.

> ... nothing she thought was necessary but to send me 2 or 3 months to a Semstress to be [taught] to make houshold linen, and having added this accomplishment to my former ingenuities, I never afterwards could find leisure for thinking of anything but to contrive and make for the family in all imaginable forms whatever was wanting, and thus I learned to make bags and sword knots long before I knew how to make Caps and furbelows. My destiney seemed now to be unalterable....[28]

In her second Autobiography, Caroline tells us that some time later she learned "grafting", that is, the ornamental weaving of fine yarns, "and washing silk stocking by way of enabling me to do this tedious kind of work which otherwise must have been put out".[29] Then, in the summer of 1766, a clandestine opportunity occurred. She made friends with a Miss Carsten who lived under the same roof and who was skilled in needlework; indeed, she "excelled in almost every article of ornamental and fancy works that could be thought of".[30] Miss Carsten was consumptive and could not sleep, and she was happy to exchange lessons in the early hours for the comfort of Caroline's company. When Miss Carsten was awake and ready for her pupil, she would indicate this by coughing at her window, and Caroline would slip out of the Herschel apartment and join her. Their rendezvous must have been at dawn, for Caroline says that on most days they were able to spend hours together, even though by seven o'clock she would have to be home and ready to begin her household chores. This happy arrangement came to an end at Michaelmas 1766, when the Herschels moved to another apartment.

Caroline was careful to assemble examples of her handiwork for a possible future employer:

> Though I had neither time nor means for producing anything imediately either
> for shew or use, I was content with keaping Samples of all possible pattern in
> needlework, Beeds, bugles, Hors-hair &c. For I could not help feeling troubled
> sometimes about my future destiny in case I should loose my dear Father, and
> my Brothers getting Married; for I could not bear the idea of being turned
> into a Abigal[31] or Housmaid, and thought that with the above, and such like
> acquirements with a little Notion of Müsic, I might obtain a place as Governess
> in some Family where the want of knowing French would be no objection.[32]

Isaac died the following March, distraught at the situation in which he was
leaving his dependents, and depriving Caroline of the one resident member of
the family who set store by her education and development. The outlook for the
seventeen-year-old Caroline was now bleak indeed. The ability to read and write,
some modest skills in needlework, and an over-familiarity with cleaning and cooking, represented the sum-total of Caroline's equipment for the life ahead, her
"slender stock of self acquired abilities".[33]

Fortunately, Jacob arranged that summer to visit William in Bath, and during
his absence Caroline's household duties reduced to the point where she ventured
to ask her mother to let her spend a month or two away from home learning millinery. Jacob graciously gave his consent, on condition that Caroline was to limit
herself to making her own hats. Tense negotiations then ensued as to how much
Caroline was to pay for her lessons, and eventually a bargain was struck at the
nominal rate of one thaler per month.[34] On such terms Caroline did not expect to
be treated as an equal of the genteel ladies who were paying much more, but for
once she was lucky. Not only did the lady in charge prove as generous in spirit as
she was in pocket, but Caroline unknowingly made a friend among the other pupils
who would one day become her closest confidant.[35]

When this brief arrangement came to its conclusion, Caroline found she had
been more than welcome: she was invited back "anytime as a visitor, to work with
the juvenile party for my future improvement".[36] But Anna would not hear of it;
and much though Caroline would have loved to accept the invitation, she charac-
teristically felt pangs of conscience at the problems her absence from home was
creating for her mother.[37]

Caroline did not bear fools easily, and for her the summer of 1768 was marred
by the arrival of a country cousin who was to benefit from Anna's instruction in the
weeks before her marriage. This well-meaning girl grew fond of Caroline, but her
affection was not reciprocated: a foretaste of the life-long difficulties Caroline was
to experience in establishing human relationships outside her immediate family,
not least with women. To her annoyance, the little time that she had to herself for
reading and even practising the violin was now taken up by this country cousin.
And Alexander was forever getting into adolescent scrapes, and using his unwilling
sister as a confidant.[38]

It was now time for Jacob to return from Bath, and Caroline made household linen in anticipation of his requirements.[39] Meanwhile the family was forced to make another of their many changes of apartment, for a forge was set up underneath their present home and the noise of the blacksmith drowned out the attempts of the brothers to practise music.[40]

Caroline rarely left Hanover, but the invitation to a cousin's wedding occasioned a visit to Hameln. She spent one day in sightseeing round the fortifications, and then was escorted to Sophia's home at Coppenbrügge *en route* for Hanover, where she arrived after a week's absence, glad to be back in her predictable routine.[41]

Jacob's return, however, was delayed because he had dedicated a set of sonatas to Queen Charlotte and was to attend at Court to receive his reward from his patron.[42] Caroline spent the winter of 1768/9 exploiting her newly-acquired skills in needlework, making him a set of ruffles of Dresden work.[43] Jacob's arrival at the end of July 1769, together with Dietrich who had also been in Bath, added greatly to the domestic chores, and Anna hired a servant to help her cope. The family quarters were now so cramped that Caroline had to share her bed with the servant, an intimacy that she much resented.[44]

In the months that followed, the tensions between Jacob and Anna increased and soured the atmosphere in the home:

> ... my Mother and Jacob seldom were satisfied with each other, and ... I began to feel great anxiety about my future destination; for I saw that all my exertions would not save me from becoming a burden to my brothers; and I had by this time imbibed too much pride for submitting to take a place as a Ladies maid, and for a Governess I was not qualified for want of knowledge in Languages.[45]

And, as her father had warned her, the diminutive, pox-marked girl had little hope of a proposal of marriage. Looking back on these times with the perspective of old age, Caroline was to write:

> ... there was no kind of ornamental needlework, knotting, platting hard, stringing beads & bugles &c of which I did not make samples by way of securing the art. But as it was my lot to be the Ashenbröthle [Aschenbrödel = Cinderella] of the Family (being the only girl) I could never find time for improving myself in many things I knew and which (after all) proved of no use to me afterwards, except what little I knew of Music, being just able to play the 2^d Violin of an overture of easy Quartetto which my Father took pleasure in teaching me. NB when my mother was not at home. Amen! I must think no more of those times....[46]

Her prospects were gloomy, and Caroline took refuge — somewhat surprisingly — in "making and altering various articles of furniture",[47] as the spring of 1771 gave way to summer and the next change of apartment neared.

But rescue plans were in train. At Bath William and Alexander were well aware of the need to rescue their sister from Anna's clutches. And William himself could make good use of her services. At Leeds he had lodged with the Bulman family, and the arrangement had proved such a success that soon after his arrival in Bath he had secured Mr Bulman a position there and invited him and his wife and daughter to live with him once more and help run his home. But he did not know how long this arrangement would last; and in any case the Bulmans did not manage his accounts, copy music for him, train his choirs, or do any of the myriad routine chores that took up so much of his time. These duties could confidently be entrusted to the totally reliable Caroline. But on what pretext could Caroline be brought to Bath?

All the boys of the family had become accomplished violinists, but Anna had blocked her husband's attempts to give similar training to Caroline. Yet Caroline might — just might — have an undiscovered talent for singing. The chances that this German girl of humble origins might acquire the confidence and skill to stand in front of an aristocratic audience in Bath and deliver in English such arias as "I know that my Redeemer liveth" must have been vanishingly small; but this was the best excuse her brothers in Bath could find for her joining them there.[48]

We can picture the astonishment of Caroline in October 1771 when a letter arrived from William, proposing that she pay him an extended visit, to see if she had the makings of a soloist in Handel's oratorios. What a transformation in life was now dangled before her! Of course she was overjoyed, and at once began to practise singing, with a gag in her mouth as the prevailing wisdom dictated. Jacob, to do him justice, was at first taken with the idea; but then the absurdity of the proposal struck him, and he turned to ridicule.[49]

Hedging her bets, Caroline now set to work to knit ruffles. If she stayed, they were for William as a thank-you present; if she left, they would be a parting gift for Jacob. For Anna and Dietrich she knitted two years' supply of cotton stockings.[50]

> In this manner I tried to still the compunction I felt at leaving relatives who I feared would lose some of their comforts by my desertion; and nothing but the belief of returning to them full of knowledge and accomplishments could have supported me in the parting moment....[51]

Not only that, but Caroline, a grown woman in her twenties, felt she must have the permission of her eldest brother if she was to go.

As it chanced, when William arrived in Hanover on 2 August 1772, determined to press matters to a conclusion, Jacob was away on duty with the Court Orchestra and so prevented from taking part in the discussions — or rather, negotiations, for William overcame Anna's misgivings by settling on her an annuity for substitute help in the home, which would be paid by Alexander and himself.[52] It is hard to see how Jacob could have prevented Caroline's departure, not least because he was on excellent terms with William; yet she was loathe to leave without his consent. But within a fortnight William would have to return to his engagements in Bath, and Caroline had to decide one way or the other. To abandon her mother and brothers without permission went against the grain, but the temptations of Bath were too great. In the first of the four pivotal decisions of her life, she accepted.

1772–1782: A CAREER BLOOMS AND FADES

Caroline's commitment to her career as a singer, not surprisingly, was to prove more enduring than William's enthusiasm for teaching her. She of course understood — perhaps it had not even merited explicit mention — that she was to make herself useful to her rescuer in whatever way she could, by helping in the running of the home and by assisting in his many-faceted musical work. But, as ill-luck would have it, William was even then developing a passion for astronomy, and for a serious amateur, astronomy was a time-consuming avocation. He was careful not to reveal to Caroline the full extent of the ambitions that were beginning to form in his mind; but he tried to whet her own appetite for astronomy by teaching her the constellations[53] as they journeyed across Holland in an open coach; and when they reached London after a traumatic crossing she noted that the shops they visited in their few hours in the capital were all those of opticians.[54]

William's immediate task was to integrate Caroline into his household, without alienating the Bulmans in the process. On the journey, therefore, he had been careful to paint a rosy picture of the household Caroline was about to join: Mrs Bulman was helpful beyond measure, and her daughter would be a companion of similar age to herself.[55] And so Mrs Bulman proved to be, although Caroline was sceptical of the usefulness of some of her wide-ranging culinary instruction.[56] With Miss Bulman, however, Caroline had little patience: since earliest childhood she herself had known nothing but poverty and a daily grind, and she found it hard to empathise with those whose upbringing had been less demanding: the girl was "very little better than an Idiot".[57]

Caroline was to share the attic of William's home with Alexander, and she hoped to find him there to greet them when she and William arrived on 27 August. But it chanced that Alexander was away on one of the musical engagements that Bath musicians traditionally undertook during the summer months, "And so I found myself all at once in a strange Country and amongst straingers" who spoke a language she did not understand.[58]

The two travellers were understandably exhausted from their stressful journey, but at breakfast on the 29th Caroline's lessons began. William began to teach her the arithmetic she needed to keep household accounts, and how to record income and outgoings: each Sunday she would be given a sum of money for the expenses of the coming week, and expected to account for it.[59] He auditioned her untrained voice, and "being very well satisfyed"[60] gave her two or three lessons each day. And so, for a month, all was well as Caroline's career made steady progress. But then the season began. She must have known that her lessons would now have to take second place to William's musical engagements, on which their livelihood depended; but she had not appreciated that in the winter months "my Brothers time was intirely taken up with Business",[61] and that if she wanted a lesson, however brief, she would have to get up early and sing to him while he was at breakfast. This was a setback, but the season would not last forever.

After six weeks in England Caroline had a smattering of English, enough for her to venture to market. In Hanover she had never been entrusted with the shopping, but now "I was sent alone among Fishwomen, Butchers basket women &c and brought home whatever in my fright I could pick up".[62] But her brothers were more understanding than she realized: Alexander secretly shadowed her steps until he saw that she was safely on her way home.[63] Home itself, however, was not without stress. William employed Betty, "a hot-headed old Welsh woman",[64] whose standards did not come up to Caroline's and whose conversation was unintelligible. As a result, "all attempts of introducing any order in our little household proved in vain".[65] As William rushed out of the house each morning after a hurried breakfast, he would leave instructions for dinner, and Caroline would have to mediate these to Betty. Summoning up her minimal reserves of tact, she presented the orders as coming from her brother, but "they were received with so much ill will"[66] that Betty gave notice and left. Never having hired a servant before, Caroline contacted an agency and without further enquiry agreed an engagement with a replacement for Betty, on a month's notice. So began the employment in the Herschel household of a succession of unsatisfactory servants, "Pickpockets and Streetwalkers"[67] among them, until a singer in William's chapel choir warned Caroline to take up references before offering anyone a job.[68]

As a result of all this domestic strife, Caroline found herself deprived not only of the expected lessons from William, but even of the leisure time to practise on her own. Writing in extreme old age, she remembers that "I was wexed at being thus so pittifully interrupted in my practise".[69] Worse was to follow: "... because after the beginning of June Bath becomes intirely empty I hoped and expected my Brother would now help me on a little more in my Musical practice",[70] but Caroline discovered to her dismay that William's interest in astronomy had developed into a passion that took priority over her singing lessons. After retiring to bed with his astronomy books, William's "first thought on rising were — on how to obtain Instruments for viewing those objects (of whom he had been reading) Himself...".[71] As a result, "About this time I was much hindered in my practice by my help being continually wanted in the executing of the various contrivances and I was in making a Tube for a 15 feet refracting Telescope[72] of pastebord sometimes assisted by my brother Alexander". Not only that, but "... to my sorrow I saw almost every room turned into a workshop".[73] This was to set the pattern for the years to come: William's existence would revolve around his twin passions, music and astronomy, with music taking priority during the winter season and astronomy during the summer. It was not that he consciously reneged on his promise to his sister to see if she had the makings of an oratorio singer: he paid for her to have dancing lessons,[74] and laid out ten guineas for the dress she would need as a soloist performer,[75] and in the winter of 1783/4 he even sent her to London to hear the best singers in the capital.[76] It was simply that his time was now doubly precious to him, and when it came to disposing of it Caroline's career as a singer came low in his order of priorities.

The visit to London was for Caroline a traumatic experience that she remembered vividly to the end of her days.[77] William did not realize how ill-at-ease his little sister felt when in polite society. Bath was bad enough. The Marchioness of Lothian, a frequent visitor to the Herschel home, used to give Caroline tickets to plays, and William's friend Mrs Colbrook would take her to the Pump Room, "But I ever felt most happy on returning from these places at the thought that I was not obliged to be every night pushed about in a gentil crowd".[78] It happened that Mrs Colbrook had legal business in London, and the well-intentioned William asked her to take Caroline with her, and to be sure to go to the opera.

First Caroline needed suitable dresses. "My Brother had left it to Mrs Bulman to make such additions to my Cloathing as were necessary for such an excurtion." Next, the young woman who in Hanover had never spent a groschen unnecessarily would need pocket money for the theatre and even for having her hair done, not to mention gratuities; William "gave me 12 Gueneas, in case we went to any Public places that I might pay for my Tickets Hair-dresser &c.".[79] All this went against the grain for Caroline.

On top of which, Mrs Bulman took it upon herself to exceed her brief. Convinced for some reason that William would shortly marry Mrs Colbrook, she "very officiously tuck care to fill my head with doubts and fears about the impossility of pleasing this wimsical Lady" while they were in London together.[80] With a Caroline over-anxious to make a good impression on her future sister-in-law, the visit was to have lasted two weeks. This was bad enough. But heavy snow fell, the roads became impassable, and Caroline found herself trapped in London with Mrs Colbrook for a further month. Not surprisingly, her money ran out. She borrowed two guineas from Mrs Colbrook, and then (as William had instructed her) applied to the Hanoverian agent in London for a further loan. The agent was "not at home", which was probably the truth; but Caroline began to suspect this was a white lie and that she was not regarded as trustworthy. There she was, trapped in London and penniless. Fortunately the snow retreated, and the roads were cleared. William managed to sort the finances out by correspondence, and on the final morning of their stay Caroline was able to collect five guineas from the agent. But then she got lost on the way back to their lodgings, and finally arrived to find the coach's departure overdue and Mrs Colbrook waiting for her with ill-concealed impatience. They would have to make up time on the journey.

Worse was to follow. Mrs Colbrook's servant, who rode alongside the carriage on horseback, was taken ill, at which his mistress descended into hysterics. But surely all would be well when Caroline reached the sanctuary of her Bath home. Not a bit of it! Alexander was absent, William in bed with fever, and the door was opened by "a huge blier-eyed" servant whom Caroline had never seen before.

But despite these travails, Caroline had had some memorable experiences in London, and even in her nineties she remembered them with pleasure. She and Mrs Colbrook went to the theatres at Drury Lane and Covent Garden, though by chance they missed the last performance ever by the great Shakespearean actor

David Garrick. They frequently attended the opera, as William had instructed, and one of the singers they heard was the famous castrato Giuseppe Millico. To the Pantheon in Oxford Street, a venue for balls and masquerades that had opened in 1772 and was to be destroyed by fire in 1792,[81] they went twice, part of an audience that Caroline reckons numbered a thousand.

Some mornings they went to auctions, which Caroline found boring. On occasion her opinion was solicited, but the only time she ventured to give it was to recommend the purchase of a pair of carriage horses. To her mortification these later proved to be blind.[82]

Not surprisingly, on her return Caroline was sufficiently out of sorts for Mrs Bulman to send for a doctor, "but I knew that for removing the ill Efects acquired by six weeks Fasionable and harassing Town life a return to my accustomed occupations at home would be the only necessary remedy".[83]

But listening to the best singers that London could offer was one thing; emulating them was another, and called for dedicated practice guided by a competent teacher. A decade or so before, back in her Hanoverian scullery, Caroline had felt "troubled sometimes about my future destiny". Now the same worries crowded in on her:

> But meanwhile I could not help feeling some uneasiness about my future prospects, for all the time my Brother could spare from his publick business and attending on his Scholars was completely filled up with Optical and Mechanical works; and the fine nights with viewing the Heavens, so that I could not hope for receiving any lessons or direction in my practising....[84]

Indeed, she had his company only when she was making herself useful in the manufacture of astronomical gadgets, or reading to him to relieve the boredom while he was polishing a mirror, or serving him food so that he could eat without interrupting his work. Doing what she could to sustain her career, she "applied each moment I could find in practising by myself by given rooles". Sunday mornings and evenings she helped William with the chapel choir; Wednesday and Saturday mornings she went shopping, and in the afternoons to her dancing teacher. In the winter, after the season resumed, she would be needed to copy the innumerable parts required by the orchestra and choristers for the oratorios that were so important a part of Bath and Bristol musical life. William, ever intrigued by a practical problem, devised a desk for her so that she could write standing up and so avoid damage to her voice.

In the spring of 1777, as Easter neared and the oratorio season approached its climax, Caroline found herself having to train the choir in her own drawing room, while herself preparing at long last to perform as soloist. On 5 March 1777, she sang for the first time as a principal, in a performance of Handel's *Judas Maccabaeus* at the New Assembly Rooms in Bath, and other oratorios followed on the 12th and 19th. The proprietor of the Bath Theatre pronounced her an ornament to the stage. At long last her career as a soprano soloist was back on track.

We can imagine her dismay when the season ended and William once more abandoned music for astronomy. But with the autumn the season resumed, and at the end of the year the infighting among concert promoters in Bath resulted in the departure of William's rivals, so that he became responsible for concerts at both Assembly Rooms and in Bristol as well. Caroline regularly featured as a singer, and on 15 April 1778 she appeared in *Messiah* as first soloist.

It was to prove the occasion for the second of the four pivotal decisions she made in her life, one that was to have important consequences for the history of astronomy. After the concert a member of the audience came up to her and invited her to sing in Birmingham. With rehearsals and performance, this would have involved her in several days away from William: a lady on her own, and as soloist the centre of attention. And who knows where this might have led? At long last Caroline had the career-break she had dreamed of.

But courage failed her, with the excuse that "I never intended to sing anywhere but where my Brother was the conductor".[85] Fate had offered her the chance of a lifetime and she had spurned it. She was well aware that it was William who had rescued her from the scullery and, able though he was, he could not achieve his ambitions (whatever they might eventually prove to be) without her assistance. Not only that, but she had been accustomed from infancy to being ordered about by her mother and brothers; and she had been in this alien land for little more than five years. William was nearing the age of forty, twelve years her senior and a man of outstanding abilities and brimming with self-confidence; and he always had (and always would) issue instructions to his little sister in the confident belief that she would obey without question. Insecure as she was, nature and nurture had conditioned her to play second fiddle in life.

The decision was hers alone. And yet, being human and therefore illogical, this would not stop her from harbouring an enduring grudge against William for the failure of her career. Thus when writing her first Autobiography she decided on further consideration to destroy the early pages telling of the French occupation of Hanover and to confine herself to family matters, so that Dietrich

> may also see how vainly his poor Sister has been strugling through her whole life, for acquiring a little knowledge and a few accomplishments; as might have saved her from wasting her time in the performance of such drudgeries and laborious works as her good Father never intended to see her grow up for.[86]

Her complaint relates not merely to her childhood in Hanover, or to her years as a would-be singer in Bath, but to "her whole life", during the last four decades of which she had been William's astronomical assistant.

The opportunity of making a musical career that came her way in April 1778 was never to return. In the months that followed, Caroline found it impossible to sustain her standards as a singer in the face of William's increasing obsession with astronomy. When *Messiah* was performed a year later she was demoted to second soloist, and the following year most of the principals were brought from

London: standards had risen, and Caroline was now restricted to working with the chorus.[87]

Towards the end of 1779 the Herschels moved from 19 New King Street to 27 Rivers Street.[88] By now William had begun not only to make telescopes but systematically to observe with them. Early in March 1781 William decided to return to their former home at 19 New King Street, but on the 13th, when he made the momentous discovery of Uranus, Caroline was still at Rivers Street. William had let the ground floor to a millinery business, in which he had bought Caroline a share. But the business had failed — for one thing, it was too far from the centre of town — and the stock was being sold off. To make sure the Herschels were not defrauded by their partners, Caroline was keeping a watchful eye on the disposals.

This took until the 21st. Easter was now three weeks away, and in Passion week there were two oratorios to be given in Bath and repeated in Bristol, a heavy schedule. Once again the principals were brought from London, and Caroline did no more than lead the sopranos.

With the end of the season, astronomy took over once more. William's fame as an observer was beginning to spread; professionals were taking note of the remarkable amateur talent that had appeared in their midst, and new-found friends were going out of their way to alert him to the latest research. In these days before photocopiers, Caroline's ability to copy flawlessly and clearly proved invaluable:

> my Brother was obliged to make trial of my abilities in copying for him Catalogues, Tables, &c. and sometimes whole papers which were lent him for his perusal, of which among others was one of Mr Michel and a Cat. of Christian Mayer in Latin which kept me employed when my Brother was at the Telescope at night; for when I found that a hand sometimes was wanted when any particular measures were to be made with the Lamp micrometer &c. and a fire to be kept in, and a dish of Coffe necessary during a long nights watching; I undertook with pleasure what others might have thought a hardship.[89]

1782–1788: THE ASSISTANT ASTRONOMER

The 1781/2 season ended with a performance of *Messiah* on 1 May 1782. On the 19th, Whitsunday, an anthem by William was performed at St Margaret's chapel; William was at the organ, and Caroline sang the treble solo. As she later noted wryly, in so doing "I opened my mouth for the last time before the public",[90] for early the following week William obeyed a royal summons to London, ostensibly to demonstrate his favourite telescope to King George III. George was under pressure from William's allies to find a way to enable him to give up music and devote himself to astronomy; perhaps — or perhaps not — Caroline was asked if she was willing to have her own life transformed in the process. Certainly there was no knowing where William might end up — the King's observatory at Kew was the destination favoured by his allies, Hanover was mooted at one point, in the event it proved to be Windsor. The letters sent by William to Bath during his extended absence kept Caroline and Alexander informed as to how he was spending his time, but there is not the slightest hint that Caroline was consulted about the whereabouts of his — and her — future home.

Nor was she consulted about the home itself. Having agreed terms with the King, William hastily cast about the Windsor area for a suitable property to rent and alighted on one in the nearby village of Datchet. In less than a fortnight he had returned to Bath, wound up his affairs there, and arranged the transport of their belongings to their new house.

The property was suitable in William's eyes because it had ample space for the workshops, library and viewing areas that he needed. To Caroline it was far from suitable. Indeed she was aghast at finding herself expected to run "the ruins of a place". There was no sign of the servant William had hired, because she was in prison for theft. And as for prices:

> the first time I went to make markets I was astonished at the dearness of every article and saw at once that my Brothers Scheeme of living cheep in the country (as jokingly he said) on Eggs and Bacon would come to nothing; for at Bath I had the week before bougth from 16 to 20 Eggs for 6^d, here I could not get no more than five for 4^d Butchers meat was 2½^d and 3^d per pound dearer; and the only Butcher at Datched would besides not give honest weight and we were obliged to deal all the time we lived there at Windsor. Coals were more than double the price. O dear! I thought what shall we do with 200 [pounds] a year! After Rent and Taxes are deducted; the lat[t]er were in consequence of the overcharged rent (and there being upwards of 30 Windows on the premises) enormous....[91]

Nor were these the only drawbacks. For all her shyness, Caroline was used to a life where there was endless coming and going of visitors — music pupils, choirs to be trained, and latterly astronomers amateur and professional. Datchet by contrast was a backwater; and when William was absent, Caroline was "left solely to confuse myself with my own thoughts, which were anything else but cheerful; for I found I was to be trained for an assistant Astronomer".[92] William was brilliant at man-management, but his sister-management skills were non-existent. Caroline was not consulted about her future role, she was not even informed: William took her acquiescence for granted and left her to infer her fate from the instructions he gave her.

Much of the time she was to act as 'gofer' for him when he was observing. In this she passed muster:

> I had ... the comfort to see that my Brother was satisfied with my endevours in assisting him when he wanted another person either to run to the Clocks, writing down a memorandum, fetching and carr[y]ing instruments, or measuring

the ground with poles &c. &c. of which something of the kind every moment would occur.[93]

But when William did not need her, Caroline was to observe on her own account. He made for her a little "sweeper" consisting of the simplest of refractors mounted against a vertical axis about which it rotated. With the instrument set to a given altitude, Caroline could 'sweep' horizontally around the sky through a complete circle. She was to look out for anything of interest: double stars, clusters, nebulae, as well as comets. But her recollection in old age was that "I was to sweep for Comets",[94] and William says explicitly that as early as 30 September 1782, only her second night of observations, she was sweeping for comets.[95] But not with any enthusiasm, for

> it was not till the last two months of the same year before I felt the least encouragement for spending the starlight nights on a grass-plot covered by dew or hoar frost without a human being near enough to be within call.[96]

Experience was to bring home to them two shortcomings in Caroline's current practice as an observer. First, the instrument was awkward to use, because Caroline had of course to keep her eye to the eyepiece as she rotated the refractor about the vertical axis, and so she had herself to rotate awkwardly with it. Second, William had not yet taken on board the fundamental distinction between permanent and transient phenomena in the night sky. A double star, say, or a nebula, is permanently in place and available for study, night after night, year after year; and so it can be tackled at leisure with the best instrument available of the appropriate type, and it matters little if the instrument's field of view is restricted. A comet, by contrast, is here today and gone tomorrow, a transient and usually unforeseen visitor, intercepted most readily by an urgent sweep of large regions of sky with a wide-angle telescope. Caroline's sweeper (like its successors) was appropriate for the search for comets, not for the permanent objects in the night sky; but it would take time for them to realize this.

The first shortcoming was of course immediately obvious, and the ingenious William, impressed by Caroline's early successes as an observer, devised her an altogether more suitable instrument. At a Newtonian reflector the observer has his eye to the eyepiece inserted in the side of the tube near the top. Caroline's new, purpose-built sweeper was a Newtonian in which the bottom of the tube rotated about the top, in a vertical plane, moved by strings pulled (and later released) by means of a handle under the control of the observer. Because the upper end rotated but did not otherwise move, the same was true of the eyepiece, and so Caroline could sit motionless, viewing in turn the segments of a vertical strip of sky, as she wound in the string and slowly moved the tube from the vertical to the horizontal. Then, shifting the instrument to face a little to the left or right, she would sweep the next strip of sky, this time from the horizontal to the vertical; and so on. It was a masterpiece of simple, functional design. Caroline used the new sweeper for the first time on 4 July 1783 and it remained her favourite instrument; when she retired to Hanover in 1822 after William's death, she took the sweeper with her, and its optics are today in a Hanoverian museum.[97]

The limitations of Caroline's little refractor as a tool in the search for nebulae and the like were masked by the astonishing success Caroline enjoyed with what was little more than a toy. On her second night of observations, 30 September 1782, she came across several double stars and also a nebula that proved to be no. 27 in Charles Messier's famous list (that is, M 27) but which William had never previously seen. On 13 October she saw M 36 and on the 29th, M 13 and M 37.

In the depth of the coming winter, which was much more severe than those Windsor experiences today, Caroline's nights of observations become less frequent, but her observations on 23 January include Praesepe, the 'Beehive Cluster' of stars, and her comments on it are revealing. William was at that time convinced that he had observed changes in the Orion Nebula, which must therefore be a nearby cloud of nebulosity rather than an immensely distant and vast star system. Mathematicians had long used Newton's inverse square law of gravitational attraction to explain the movements of the Moon and planets, and John Michell had shown that double stars were so numerous that many must be companions in space held together by gravitational attraction or a similar force. William suspected that such attractive forces might have led to the formation of stars by condensation from nebulosity, and

The optics (finder, mirror, eyepieces and flat) of the purpose-built 'sweeper' that William made for Caroline in the summer of 1783, and which she later took with her to Hanover. Courtesy of the Historisches Museum in Hanover.

it seems that on this evening — one of the few occasions when Caroline displayed an interest in astronomy as a science — Caroline herself investigated whether there were traces of nebulosity still to be seen in the vicinity of the cluster: "Look'd at the Nebula in Cancer for half an hour, saw nothing nebulous; but they are all very distinct little stars." Despite the hardships involved, she was beginning to enjoy observing: "Began at the above Cluster and made a horizontal sweep all around, I spent above an hour upon this sweep, but found nothing remarkable. It was too cold, therefore could not continue my observations. A pretty strong frost."[98]

On 26 February she encountered another nebula, and this time in their respective notebooks both she and William commented: "Messier has it not." The sometime professional soprano had, it seemed, discovered a nebula hitherto unknown to science. They were in fact mistaken, for the nebula was M 93. However, a few minutes later she found another nebula, and again both commented, "Messier has it not"; but this time they were right: it was the nebula we now know as NGC 2360.

The consequences of this night's work were little short of epoch-making; not because of the two nebulae Caroline had seen, but because she had demonstrated to her brother than the mysterious nebulae and clusters were so numerous that specimens could be discovered by an inexperienced observer using the most rudimentary of instruments. And so, a week later, on 4 March William recorded his momentous decision "to sweep the heaven for Nebulas and Clusters of stars". Astronomy was soon to be transformed.

During 1783, Caroline by her own reckoning discovered fourteen nebulae and clusters,[99] and she was later to find three more. To disentangle her claims and identify her genuine discoveries is no easy task;[100] but this is in any case to undertake a work of piety, for individually her discoveries left little trace. If — and only if — William later came across the same object, and if Caroline afterwards realized she had seen it before, the initials "C.H." would be inserted in William's catalogue; but this added nothing to the scientific value of the catalogue. If William never came across the object, the record of its discovery would languish in Caroline's papers, one day to be exhumed by the present writer.

This modern work of piety yielded an unexpected bonus. On 30 July 1783 Caroline observed "a rich spot" inside the little triangle of stars 3, 4 and 7 in the constellation Pegasus. Some four weeks later, on 24 August, she again observed "a rich spot", this time not far away, between the neighbouring stars γ and δ in Equuleus. Caroline nowhere else writes of "a rich spot"; and today there is no nebula or cluster that she might have observed in either of these well-defined locations. It seems probable, therefore, that Caroline unwittingly observed a comet that has until now been unknown to astronomy.[101]

In the autumn of 1783 William commissioned his new 20-ft reflector, and for some weeks he used it single-handedly to search for nebulae and clusters. But this required him to use artificial light to note down any discoveries, and it would then be some time before his eyes were once more adjusted to the dark. The solution, arrived at at the turn of the year, was to enlist the help of Caroline, who was to sit at a desk beside a window ready to write down William's comments as he shouted them out, and to note other circumstances of the observation. A French visitor describes her at work:

> I arrived at Mr. Herschel's about ten o'clock.... Instead of the master of the house, I observed, in a window at the farther end of the room, a young lady seated at a table, which was surrounded with several lights; she had a large book open before her, a pen in her hand, and directed her attention alternately to the hands of a pendulum-clock, and the index of another instrument placed beside her, the use of which I did not know. She afterwards noted down her observations.
>
> I approached softly on tiptoe, that I might not disturb a labour, which seemed to engage all the attention of her who was engaged in it; and, having got close behind her without being observed, I found that the book she consulted was the Astronomical Atlas of Flamsteed, and that, after looking at the indexes of both the instruments, she marked, upon a large manuscript chart, points which appeared to me to indicate stars.
>
> This employment, the hour of the night, the youth of the fair student, and the profound silence which prevailed, interested me greatly. At last she turned round her head, accidentally, and discovered how much I was afraid to disturb her; she rose suddenly, and told me she was very sorry I had not informed her of my arrival, that she was engaged in following and recording the observations of her brother, who expected me, and who, in order that he might not lose the precious opportunity of so fine a night, was then busy in his observatory.
>
> "My brother," said Miss Caroline Herschel, "has been studying these two hours; I do all I can to assist him here. That pendulum marks the time, and this instrument, the index of which communicates by strings with his telescopes, informs me, by signs which we have agreed upon, of whatever he observes. I mark upon that large chart the stars which he enumerates, or discovers in particular constellations, or even in the most distant parts of the sky." ...
>
> Placed at the upper end of his telescope, when the indefatigable astronomer discovers in the most deserted parts of the sky a nebula, or a star of the least magnitude, invisible to the naked eye, he informs his sister of it, by means of a string which communicates with the room where she sits; upon the signal being given, the sister opens the window, and the brother asks her whatever information he wants. Miss Caroline Herschel, after consulting the manuscript tables before her, replies, brother, search near the star *Gamma, Orion*, or any other constellation which she has occasion to name. She then shuts the window, and returns to her employment.[102]

In William's revised method of sweeping, the reflector normally faced due south, and William kept watch for nebulae as the rotation of the Earth brought hitherto unexamined areas of sky into view. When he found a nebula, he would specify its position in relation to a nearby star (essentially in the form "up a bit", "left a bit"), and it would be necessary for Caroline to identify the star. It was not always easy for her to do this from Flamsteed's British Catalogue, for there the stars were arranged by constellation. To resolve the difficulty, in the first of her great desk-based contributions to astronomy, Caroline prepared a catalogue of stars by 'zones' of North Polar Distance — that is, by their angular distances from the Celestial North Pole (and then in the order in which they presented themselves to the observer). Since all the stars that were currently coming into William's view were at much the same distance from the Pole, her manuscript catalogue would allow her easily to identify them for him one by one.

After each night's observing Caroline would write up a fair copy of the notes she had taken, and in due course she would organize the nebulae they had discovered into catalogues for publication in *Philosophical Transactions*. She similarly prepared printer's copies of all William's numerous other published papers, which in the modern edition fill two huge quarto volumes.[103] Her surviving transcriptions of these hundreds and hundreds of pages of words and symbols are well-nigh faultless; and William's monumental achievement in astronomy would have been greatly hampered — indeed, blighted — had he not had the selfless services, day and night, of his devoted sister.

Caroline's work as night-time amanuensis to William left her with few opportunities to observe on her own account, but one came in the summer of 1786. The King had earlier asked William to make him five 10-ft reflectors. George was also Elector of Hanover, and his patronage of astronomy extended to the electorate. He therefore decided to present one of the reflectors to Göttingen University, and he thought it would be appropriate for William to transport it there in person. A disgruntled William left on 3 July.

Caroline's night hours were now her own: "The employment of writing down the observations, when my Brother uses the 20-feet reflector, does not often allow me time to look at the heavens; but as he is now on a visit to Germany, I have taken the opportunity of his absence, to *sweep* in the neighbourhood of the sun, in search of comets...."[104] By now the two of them had come to a clear understanding of what Caroline the observer could and could not do. The permanent nebulae were for examination by William with his reflectors of great 'light-gathering power'; the permanent double stars were for William with his precision 7-ft reflector; but the transient comets were the province of Caroline, who could sweep the entire sky in only a few nights.

She swept for two hours on 19 July, and from 9 p.m. to 1 a.m. on the 24th. That evening she came across two of Messier's objects, and at first wondered if one of them might be a comet. She next observed on 1 August, and at 9.50 p.m. found an object "like a star out of focus". Within a couple of hours she was referring to it as "the comet".

In William's absence it was for her to alert the scientific community, and so she wrote to Dr Charles Blagden, Secretary of the Royal Society. On the evening of the 6th, Blagden, together with the President of the Royal Society Sir Joseph Banks, and Lord Palmerston, arrived at the Herschel home begging the favour of a view of the comet. William returned on the 16th to discover what his little sister had achieved on her own account during his absence — and to find a summons to Windsor Castle to demonstrate to the Royal Family "the first lady's comet".[105]

The diminutive, pock-scarred Caroline was now in her middle thirties, and her father's gloomy forecast of her prospects of marriage was proving correct: she had learned to live her life without a hint of romance. She found fulfilment in service to her revered, if self-centred, older brother, whose home she managed and in whose great astronomical campaigns she played a subordinate but essential role. But then William began to take an increasing interest in their neighbour, the recently-widowed Mary Pitt, and in May 1788 William and Mary were married. Caroline was thereby banished from the centre of William's life to the periphery, from presiding over his table to occupying rooms in the cottage in the garden. Even her role as assistant astronomer now seemed less important to him.

1788–1797: THE COMET HUNTRESS

Caroline was outraged as her world fell apart. She felt betrayed. Mary was rich, and William was at last in a position to offer Caroline a salary; but she had had enough of brotherly handouts:

> I refused my dear brother's proposal (at the time he resolved to enter the married state) of making me independent, and desired him to ask the King for a small salary to enable me to continue his assistant. £50 were granted to me, with which I was resolved to live without the assistance of my Brother.[106]

William had phrased his application with skill:

> Now, my good, industrious sister has hitherto supplied the place of assistant, and intends to continue to do that work. She does it indeed so much better, to my liking, than any other person I could have, that I should be very sorry ever to lose her from that office. Perhaps our gracious Queen, by way of encouraging a female astronomer, might be enduced to allow her a small annual bounty, such as 50 or 60 pounds, which would make her easy for life, so that, if anything should happen to me she would not have the anxiety upon her mind of being left unprovided for. She has often formed a wish but never had the resolution of causing an application to be made to her Majesty for this purpose; nor could I have been prevailed upon to mention it now, were it not for her evident use in the observations that are to be made with the 40 feet reflector, and the unavoidable encrease of the annual expences which, if my Sister were to decline that office would probably amount to nearly one hundred pounds more for an assistant.[107]

And so Caroline became the first salaried female in the history of astronomy.

This was to create for her problems of conscience. Caroline's Protestant work-ethic troubled her if she accepted money she felt she had not earned. But for the moment all was well. Her cottage had a flat roof ideal for observing, and for the most part her nights were her own. Not only that, but William decided to build her a more powerful sweeper, modelled on its predecessor but more than twice the focal length and more than twice the aperture. Since his earliest days as an amateur astronomer, William had been forever hankering after bigger instrumentation and "more light", and in his enthusiasm he failed to take into account Caroline's physical limitations. Being under five feet in height, she could use a Newtonian of over five feet in focal length only by standing on a stool, whereas with the existing sweeper she could observe sitting down. But at least the new instrument had a triangle of wires in the field of view, and with this she could measure the relative positions of two nearby objects, where before she had had to be content with merely estimating them.

The years that followed William's marriage were emotionally painful for Caroline but scientifically productive. William's household was now being administered by his wife, and he himself was taking a much more relaxed approach to observing. Caroline had ample time for observing on her own account, and the flat roof of her cottage provided an ideal location. Occasionally she examined the Moon in the hope of glimpsing signs of the 'volcanoes' William believed he had seen,[108] but her main task was to sweep for comets. On 21 December 1788 she discovered one almost as soon as it came into view from England. This greatly impressed Nevil Maskelyne, the Astronomer Royal: "As it came up from the south it seems that Miss Herschel lost no time in finding it, I mean that it could not have been seen much sooner even in her excellent telescope."[109] She found two more in 1790, on 7 January and 18 April, and another on 15 December 1791. After an interval of nearly two years, on 7 October 1793, she found yet another comet, but it transpired that it had been seen by Messier some ten days earlier.

Another interval of two years passed, and then on 7 November 1795 she found one more comet. This too had been seen before: not however a few days earlier, but as long ago as 1786, as Johann Franz Encke was to show over a quarter of a century later. Encke had chosen to make a study of the orbit of the comet that was first seen in November 1818 by Jean Louis Pons, and in his first attempt at the calculation, published in February 1819, he noted that the orbit was somewhat similar to that of a comet Pons had seen back in 1805. Encke continued to analyse both orbits, and came to the conclusion that the comets were one and the same. By May 1819 he had further identified the comet with that seen by Caroline in 1795, and in June with the comet observed by Pierre Méchain in January 1786. Encke's Comet, as we now know it, has a period of only 3.3 years; it returned as predicted in 1822, reaching perihelion on almost the day that Encke had calculated.

Caroline's last comet, which she saw with her naked eye on 14 August 1797, was something of an anticlimax, for not surprisingly it was seen by two other observers the same night. But it gave her a chance to demonstrate the lengths to which her devotion to astronomy took her.

The physical nature of comets, and their function in the cosmos, were questions of great interest to astronomers, and the more mathematically inclined attempted to calculate their orbits. A comet was visible from Earth only for the brief interval during which it rounded the Sun and returned again to outer space, and usually it was necessary to assume that the orbit had the simple form of a parabola (in which case the comet would never be seen again). This indeed was what Encke had first done with his calculation of the orbit of his eponymous comet. Even so, if the job was worth doing it was worth doing well; and Maskelyne was torn between admiration for Caroline (in 1800 he presented her with a field-glass and a pair of binoculars to aid her searches) and exasperation, first at any delay that occurred before he and other professionals learned of the sighting of a new comet, and second at the imprecision with which Caroline would describe her observations of its position on the nights before she had been able to hand it over to Maskelyne and colleagues.

It chanced that her 1797 discovery took place when William was away, and so it was up to Caroline to inform Maskelyne, and as quickly as possible. She decided to take the bull by the horns, or more exactly the horse by the reins, and simply herself ride all the way from Slough to London, and then on to the observatory at Greenwich:

> I have so little faith in the expedition of messengers of all descriptions that I undertook to be my own ... but unfortunately I undertook the task with only the preparation of one hour's sleep, and having in the course of five years never rode above two miles at a time, the twenty to London, and the idea of six or seven more to Greenwich in reserve, totally unfitted me for any action [such as notifying the President of the Royal Society as she passed through the capital].[110]

At nights Caroline swept when the weather and moonlight were favourable, but in the daytime she had leisure, and in 1795 William "recommended" that she turn her methodical mind to defects in John Flamsteed's great British Catalogue of stars, the bible of all observers. More than a decade before, Caroline had used the Catalogue to prepare her own zone catalogue, listing the stars that William might expect to encounter as he swept; but they were both puzzled by discrepancies between the contemporary heavens and the stars as catalogued by Flamsteed. At first William suspected that the heavens had changed — that some stars had vanished while others had newly appeared, and others again had altered in brightness. But he soon began to wonder whether the British Catalogue contained errors, generated by the copyists who had transcribed the original observations by Flamsteed, or by the printers themselves. The problem was that there was no index that would allow the user to check an entry in the British Catalogue, which formed the third volume of Flamsteed's great opus, against the observations on which the entry was based, which were to be found in the second volume. Here was a task ideally suited to the meticulous Caroline, with her near-infallible reliability when it came to transcribing numbers.

The work took her two years. She found 561 stars that had been omitted from the British Catalogue by oversight: the catalogue listed three thousand stars, but should have contained three-and-a-half thousand. She also identified a number of other errors. But the core of her work was an index that allowed the user to check a catalogue entry against the (one or more) observations on which it was based. No innovative brilliance was required for the task, no astronomical insights, merely unremitting dedication and concentration: humdrum talents, perhaps, but ones possessed by Caroline and by her alone.

Maskelyne recognized that Caroline was transforming the British Catalogue into a work in which the observer could have full confidence, and he persuaded the Royal Society to publish her lists at its own expense. This was a public compliment indeed, and Caroline was understandably thrilled. It had, she told Maskelyne,

> flattered my vanity not a little. You see, Sir, I do own myself to be vain because I would not wish to be singular, and was there ever a woman without vanity? — or a man either? only with this difference, that among gentlemen the commodity is generally stiled ambition.[111]

The list of omitted stars, however, was not in the format that Maskelyne would have found most useful. Caroline therefore prepared a list in the format he wanted. The copy of this that she kept for herself ran to no fewer than 25 folio pages of numbers.

No wonder that Caroline was held in such high regard among male astronomers throughout Europe. Professor Karl Seyffer of Göttingen acclaimed her as "most noble and worthy priestess of the new heavens".[112] Jérôme de Lalande of the Collège Royale in Paris had earlier nominated her for one of the prizes recently established by the Assemblée Nationale for "the most useful work or the most important discovery for the sciences or the arts".[113]

But for all the recognition that deservedly came her way, Caroline was far from happy. The only love in her life had come from her father, long dead, and from William; and William had betrayed her by his marriage and it was now Mary who had first place in his affections. Outwardly she should have been content. She had her own salary and an admired status among scientists, in an age when few if any other women could claim the same. She had comfortable quarters, ideal observing conditions, telescopes specially designed and made for her. Her brother's love for Mary did not replace his love for her, and soon she had a delightful little nephew, John, to play with. Yet Caroline was an embittered spinster. In time her antagonism towards her sister-in-law would be replaced by a deep affection, and she would be shamed into destroying what she had written about her in the 1790s. She thereby deprived us of insight into her reactions to the death of her mother Anna, and the murder of her brother Jacob. But most frustratingly of all, she leaves us guessing as to the motive for the third pivotal decision of her life: to quit her brother's home and move into lodgings.

1797–1822: COMMUTING TO WORK

Such clues as we have for Caroline's decision come from the later years of her long life. The account of the move she then wrote is chilling in its formality:

> 1797 in October I went to lodge & Board with one of my Brother's workmen (Sprat) whose wife was to attend on me. My telescopes on the roof [of her former home] to which I was to have occasionally access; as also to the room with the sweeping and observing apparatus....[114]

This has all the warmth of an agreement over access to children following a contested divorce. In notes she made concerning John's childhood, she wrote: "But after the above mentioned October [1797] we were not so frequently together, for I was obliged to exchange my habitation to another part of Slough...."[115] In writing to John in her old age she remarked that "From the end of the year 1789 [*sic*] ... I was severed from the family but occasionally passed still as a Link of the same...".[116] When John's wife questioned her about John's childhood, she excused the limitations of her reply by explaining that "when he was five I came to be detached from the family circle".[117] That either William, her beloved brother, or his wife Mary, gentlest of creatures, asked Caroline to leave is unthinkable. And Lady Lubbock's speculation[118] that she made the disastrous (and permanent) move merely because of "the accumulation of books and instruments" is risible. It must be that some unguarded comment by William or Mary, perhaps concerning Caroline's status as a guest in their home, triggered her long-standing resentment at being dependent on fraternal charity. That she lodged at first with one of William's workmen, who may well have been close at hand when the crisis occurred, confirms the suspicion that she left in a hurry. As we shall see, she behaved in just the same precipitate way in 1822 when William died.

It would not be long before Caroline repented her departure from her comfortable and convenient cottage. On the nights when she was involved in observing, either on her own account or as amanuensis to William, she had to be escorted home by the long-suffering Sprat, presumably at an hour agreed in advance and on the basis of a guess as to what the weather would be. Little wonder that she herself never again made an observation of significance. And in her daytime desk-work she suffered all the inconvenience of the commuter: "Uncommonly harassed in consequence of the loss of time necessary for going backward and forward, and not having immediate access to each book or paper at the moment when wanted."[119] Nor did the problems stop there. Writing to John Herschel's wife Margaret in 1840, she told her that "For the last 24 years of my living in England, it was amongst beings of whom I was affraid", years "[i]n which I was obliged to change my habitation no less than 7 times, which was always attended by useless expenses, and what was still more precious, loss of time...".[120] Twice bailiffs seized her landlord's possessions against payment of a debt, and Caroline narrowly escaped losing her own books and furniture.[121]

Only in 1803 did some stability return to her life, when she took rooms in what had formerly been Mary Herschel's home at Upton. The property adjoined William's, but they were separated by fields, an easy walk in daylight but dangerous at night. It was said locally that if the skies cleared unexpectedly, Caroline would rap on the window of a local boy with the request, "Please will you take me to my Broder".[122]

It is extraordinary that a quarter of a century was allowed to pass without Caroline's swallowing her pride and requesting a return to her former quarters: years in which she achieved only a fraction of what would surely have been possible had she continued to occupy the cottage in the garden. But she undertook in her lodgings one item of desk-work that would in years to come prove to be of the greatest significance.

From the start of his work as a professional observer, William had collected nebulae and clusters, not in the traditional way that astronomers set about their business, but rather as his brother Dietrich the natural historian collected butterflies. This approach was reflected in William's catalogues, in which specimens were first classified, and then listed by the date of their discovery. Such an ordering was of little use to other observers, for if Maskelyne, say, came across a nebula, he could well waste an hour searching through William's catalogues to see if it was already known.

In the catalogues, the position of each nebula was stated in terms of where it was in relation to a nearby star; and so the first step towards a unified catalogue of the nebulae would be a unified catalogue of the reference stars. William and Caroline customarily searched for nebulae with the telescope facing south; as the sky rotated overhead William would 'sweep' a little above and below a chosen elevation, so that all the objects he encountered in that sweep were at similar distances from the Celestial North Pole: part of a 'zone' of North Polar Distance. Long ago Caroline had prepared her own catalogue of possible reference stars, taking them from Flamsteed's British Catalogue and arranging them in zones of North Polar Distance (and then in the order in which the stars presented themselves to the observer). Now, at William's request,[123] she set about compiling a unified catalogue of the stars that had actually been used for reference, arranged in the same manner. But because the best part of a century had passed since the epoch of the British Catalogue, and the stars had meantime shifted position as a result of the wobble of the Earth's axis known as precession, it was agreed that she should calculate the positions of the stars as they were in the year 1800.

She was at work on the task either side of the turn of the century. Obviously she could not complete it until the sweeps themselves had come to an end. This happened in the autumn of 1802: although some areas of sky remained to be swept, William had by now lost interest and decided 'to call it a day'. Nevertheless, it seems it was not until 1818 that Caroline at last concluded her catalogue.[124] It would one day prove invaluable.

In the early years of the new century, William made the striking discovery of the existence of infra-red rays, radiation from the Sun that comes from outside the spectrum visible to human eyes. He revisited some of the double stars he had discovered two decades earlier, and found several in which the companions had orbited about each other, demonstrating that attractive forces were at work in the stellar universe. And he became obsessed, to the dismay of his friends, in the study of 'Newton's rings', a subject where he had little competence. In all this, Caroline's involvement was marginal.

In the second decade of the century, he published great papers that were reflections on the implications of his earlier explorations of nebulae and clusters, but he undertook only limited observing: he was now well into his seventies. The consequence was that Caroline was rarely needed at nighttime, and in the daytime her duties centred on preparing fair copies of papers for publication, and curating the store of observational records with whose welfare William became increasingly obsessed.

At times, however, she was called upon to provide domestic service to one or other of her surviving brothers, as she had in Hanover half a century before. In the summer of 1800, William, who had maintained his links with Bath, changed the house that he was renting there, and Caroline was directed to make the new one habitable for him. She packed her things for an extended stay in Bath, "for there I am to go",[125] as she noted with marked lack of enthusiasm. After a month she had matters sufficiently under control for her to return to the astronomy for which the King was paying her: "... by July 29th I was ready for resuming the work of recalculating sweeps, or despatching some copying, &c., which was sent me by the coach from Slough, and from the printer in London."[126] Alexander, who had remained in Bath when William and Caroline moved to the Windsor area but whose practical skills were always at his brother's service when Bath was out of season, then went to Slough for two weeks to help William repolish the mirror of the 40-ft, and "Some of my time during his absence I spent at his house on Margaret's Hill to clean and repair his furniture, and making his habitation comfortable against his return".[127]

The third brother to benefit from Caroline's ministrations was Dietrich. He paid a pleasant visit to Slough in the summer of 1806 to see his surviving siblings along with William's son John, the sole living member of his generation to bear the name of Herschel. But Dietrich was back again in England in November 1808, this time as an economic migrant and refugee from the power struggle between Napoleon and the King of Prussia. He had decided that he could not support his family as long as he was living in Hanover, and that he must work in England and send money home.

Back in 1803, Caroline had — most uncharacteristically — accepted an offer from William and Mary of £10 a quarter to supplement her royal pension. She had thereby reversed her refusal of William's offer of money at the time of his marriage, and this makes her continuing exile from William's home all the more baffling. She later maintained that she accepted the money because she had "been in a panic for my friends at Hanover",[128] and there may be truth in this. If so, now was the time to make use of the money, and so she passed it over to Dietrich for the duration of his stay. It was the first, but not the last, financial help she gave to Dietrich and his family, and when she became estranged from them in her old age, she would several times indulge her sense of outrage by calculating just how much she had given them over the years.

Dietrich's stay in England was a long one:

> From the hour of Dietrich's arrival in England till that of his departure, which was not till nearly four years after, I had not a day's respite from accumulated trouble and anxiety, for he came ruined in health, spirit, and fortune, and, according to the old Hanoverian custom, I was the only one from whom all domestic comforts were expected. I hope I have acquitted myself to everybody's satisfaction, for I never neglected my eldest [surviving] brother's business, and the time I bestowed on Dietrich was taken entirely from my sleep or from what is generally allowed for meals, which were mostly taken running, or sometimes forgotten entirely.[129]

Life was not so very different from what it had been when she was a child.

Dietrich, the sometime baby of the family, had a special place in Caroline's affections. William of course had been her rescuer and she owed him a debt that she could never repay. But he was twelve years her senior, a powerful personality who took for granted her unquestioning obedience. Since 1772 their lives had been intertwined, yet Caroline "kept to the resolution of never opening my lips to my dear brother William about worldly or serious concerns".[130] To Dietrich, however, she could open her heart.

He was not the only one. Like most celibates, Caroline felt the need of friends with whom she could share her troubles, and in 1802 this need was supplied from a most unlikely quarter. Back in Hanover, in the millinery lessons, a little girl of some ten or eleven years of age had been a fellow pupil whom Caroline had barely noticed. When Caroline on a visit to Windsor Castle was introduced to one of Queen Charlotte's entourage, a Mme Beckedorff, this lady identified herself as the little girl of long ago, and she and Caroline became firm friends: "I was soon sensible of having found what hitherto I had looked for in vain — a sincere and uninterested [disinterested] Friend, to whom I might have applied for counsel and comfort in my deserted situation."[131]

During Dietrich's extended stay in England, all of Caroline's closest family and friends — William, Alexander, Dietrich, Mme Beckedorff — were in England and within easy reach. Soon this happy state of affairs began to change. Dietrich returned to Hanover in 1812, Alexander retired there in 1816, as did Mme Beckedorff after the death of Queen Charlotte in 1818. William's health was then becoming increasingly precarious, and it was evident that Caroline must decide what she should do when eventually he died. King George III was no longer capable of ruling, but the Prince Regent had confirmed her pension, so that she had money enough for her modest needs. Caroline was a tough little lady, but this was not how she saw herself. Back in 1808 she had had a nasty scare when her doctor told her she was going blind and that she should practise to prepare herself for life with this handicap; but it proved to be a false alarm.[132] Other than this, her health was good. Yet Caroline was a healthy hypochondriac. In 1814, "I, for my part, felt that I should never be anything else but an invalid for life, but which I very carefully kept to myself, for I wished to be useful to my brother for as long as I possibly could".[133] As the years passed, and William's life neared its end, she convinced herself that she too was not long for this world. Should she remain in Slough after William's death? Mary, calm and steadfast in affection, had long since been forgiven for usurping Caroline's place, but what the two women had in common was their devotion to William. John had matured into a young man of outstanding brilliance and exceptional charm, and he had endeared himself to his aunt still further by abandoning his Cambridge career in order to become his father's apprentice in astronomy. John was indeed a model son and a cherished nephew. Yet his heart was in London; he was a leading figure in the scientific life of the capital, and one of the founders of what would become the Royal Astronomical Society. There was no role in this for an aged spinster in provincial Slough, nothing therefore to keep her in England; or so she thought.

By 1820, she had made up her mind, in the fourth and most tragic of the pivotal decisions that she made. Alexander was in Hanover, Mme Beckedorff was in Hanover, and so were Dietrich and his family:

> I sent ... thirty pounds to be laid out for a fether bed for me when after a long dreaded melancholy event [the death of William] I should be obliged to seek consolation in the busom of Diterich's family, which after the description of his wife and daughters' characters, I thought to be the only place on earth where I could find rest.[134]

Alexander died in 1821, but this did not alter Caroline's resolve, for Alexander was a bachelor whereas Dietrich had a wife and family to join in the welcome for her. She cemented her bond with Dietrich still further. As on several occasions in the past, he was in financial trouble, this time because the husband of his second daughter Sophia was "deranged"[135] and she and her children were destitute. Caroline reinforced her commitment to Hanover by making over to Dietrich her savings of £500. As she later wrote to John,

> ... you remember I parted with my little property before I left England (against your good advice) because I thought at that time I should not live a 12 month and wished to enable my Brother to save the Family of his 2nd daughter with that sum from ruin....[136]

After a lengthy decline in health, William died on 25 August 1822, and was buried a fortnight later.

Slough was now for Caroline a melancholy place, full of memories sweet and bitter. Her response was simple: to flee the scene. As John wrote to a friend,

> She has resolved on leaving England immediately and going to reside with her family in Hanover, and the expectation of preparing for her journey has been of service in distracting her attention from dwelling on its cause.[138]

Just two days after the funeral she began to dispose of her furniture and to select what she was to take with her. John urged her to wait until he had settled William's affairs and was free to escort her, but she was in a panic to put the past behind her and begin a new life elsewhere. Dietrich, to his great credit, insisted on coming to England to fetch her.

It would not be long before her conscience began to trouble her over what she came to see (perhaps with some justification) as her desertion of John. Within weeks of her precipitate departure from Slough she told him: "... believe me I would not have gone without at least having made the offer of my service for some time longer to you my dear Nephew; had I not felt that it would be in vain to struggle any longer against age and infirmity."[139] True, John had promised to revise and complete all aspects of his father's work, and this of course included the nebulae; but currently he was focusing on double stars, in partnership with James South who owned the precision instruments ideal for the task, and the two observers had no need of an amanuensis. The nebulae would come later; and then John would indeed be hampered by the lack of a Caroline.[140]

But when William died she was already into her seventies, and convinced she did not have long to live. Whether she would in fact have found the physical strength to share the night watches with John as she had with his father long ago is very doubtful; but she would surely have found other ways to help, if only by making each morning a fair copy of the previous night's observations.

One contribution of immense significance she was able to make from her desk in Hanover. As we have seen, William's catalogues of nebulae were ordered by class and the date of discovery, a format well-nigh useless to John as he set about his re-examination of his father's nebulae. John needed the nebulae arranged in zones of North Polar Distance, so that he could replicate his father's sweeps. Caroline had already taken the first step towards this by arranging the reference stars in this format; now she embarked on the straightforward but onerous task of doing the same for the nebulae whose positions were defined by the reference stars. She completed the task early in 1825, a catalogue of 104 folio pages of numbers. It was, in the words of Sir David Brewster, "an extraordinary monument of the unextinguished ardour of a lady of seventy-five in the cause of abstract science".[141] In 1828 her devotion was recognized by the award of the Gold Medal of the (Royal) Astronomical Society, and in 1835 this all-male organization elected her to Honorary Fellowship, a tribute she valued so much that she had it inscribed on her tombstone.

This aside, her absence from Slough was a self-inflicted injury that robbed her life of an on-going purpose, and separated her from the one human being to whom she felt "Motherly".[142] In Hanover her increasing alienation from nearly all of those around her — though a curse common enough in extreme old age — was exacerbated by knowing that she had only herself to blame for the emptiness of her existence. She had been lured there by roseate memories of her childhood haunts, and still more so by the family and friends awaiting her there.

Her progressive estrangement from Dietrich and his family is the saddest aspect of her life in Hanover, for she had returned to Hanover above all to be reunited with him and to enjoy the company of his family. By inviting her, and in coming to England to fetch her at a time of family bereavement and personal illness, Dietrich had demonstrated his love. All the more sad, then, to see poison entering into their relationship. As soon as they set foot together on Continental soil, Caroline found Dietrich an uncomfortable and opinionated companion, and in the four years remaining to him his health steadily declined while Caroline's sympathies came under increasing strain. Her relationship with Dietrich's family was at first excellent — on arrival in Hanover she was nothing short of delighted at the provision they had made for her — but it deteriorated fast. In 1835 she wrote to one of John's brothers-in-law:

> ... for what I have found here is a mongrel breed of the 2^d . 3^d &c generation none of which were born or even thought of at the time (1772) I exchainged my Country for that of England, and I have not been able to trace any other feeling in any of them but selfishness.[143]

She saw herself as having been deceived, lured into a Hanoverian trap by false assurances of love and companionship. Herself a woman who had grown up in poverty and had never spent a penny more than was necessary, and who justifiably saw the gift of her savings to help support Dietrich's daughter Dorothea as a gesture of exceptional kindness, she was became increasingly regretful over what she viewed as her misplaced generosity. She wrote of

> ... my arrival in Han^r at the end of Octr 1822 when I trusted to meet with love and gratitude for the sacrifice I had made before I left England by making over to Dietrich all I was worth for the benefit (not of his Wife) but of Him and his Family! Leaving myself nothing but my necessities....[144]

Persuaded that Dietrich's family were sponging on her for what they could get out of her, while they grudged every minute they spent with the lonely old woman, Caroline's resentment festered increasingly as time passed. On several occasions[145] she sat down and calculated every thaler, every gutengroschen, they had cost her, not forgetting the £10 per quarter from Mary that she had made over to Dietrich during the four years he had spent in Slough. At least she now knew "how much I have thrown away on beings to whom I was under no obligation of any kind; and among whom there is not one who would sometimes sacrifice an hour to cheer me in a long winter's evening".[146]

John visited her three times: in 1824, on his way home from one of his European tours; in 1832, when they must have discussed John's plans to explore the southern skies that William had never seen; and in 1838, immediately after his return from the Cape of Good Hope. On this occasion he took with him his young son William. It was a time of joy for Caroline: her brother's great work was now complete, and his name lived on in his grandson. But when the day came for her to say a last goodbye, she found to her dismay that John had already fled Hanover, unable to face the trauma of the farewell. "You came to take Tea with me", she was to write, "and soon left me for ever! Without taking leave!"[147]

John carefully preserved the numerous letters that Caroline wrote from Hanover, and those of the 1830s and '40s offer poignant evidence of Caroline's emotional decline as she moved into advanced old age. Mentally she was among the most blessed of mortals. She tempted fate when she drafted an epitaph that spoke of her retaining her faculties to the end, but so she did: even in her early to mid-nineties her mind was alert, her memory prodigious, her command of English exceptional, and her handwriting as lucid as ever. But this "poor solitary old maid",[148] as she saw herself, was an unquiet soul. In her letters she constantly complains about her health, as old people do, even though she was seldom ill. She is obsessed about the disposal of her effects, repeatedly assuring John that she will leave the money needed to satisfy her obligations to her faithful maidservant Betty and to members of the family, as well as to meet the cost of her funeral. And she bewails how lonely she is in "Horrible Hannover".[149]

A gloomy view of life came readily to Caroline. "The whole of yesterday", she wrote in 1839, "I had no other prospect but that it would have been the last of the days of sorrow, trouble, and disappointment I have spent from the moment I had any recollection of my existence, which is from between my third and fourth year".[150] A few days later she spoke of the "solitary and useless life I have led these seventeen years, all owing to not finding Hanover, nor anyone in it, like what I left...".[151]

William's reputation was of course sacrosanct. She asked John to re-examine a region of Scorpio that had attracted William's interest. He did so, and found it full of clusters of stars. But this was the wrong answer: "It is not clusters of stars I want you to discover in the body of the Scorpion (or thereabout), for that does not answer my expectation, remembering having once heard your father, after a long awful silence, exclaim, 'Hier ist wahrhaftig ein Loch im Himmel!' ['Here indeed is a hole in the heavens!']"[152] The tactful John lost no time in finding both clusters and spaces devoid of stars.[153]

The achievements of Lord Oxmantown (later Earl of Rosse) in building reflectors at his castle in King's County, Ireland, that dwarfed the 20-ft with which William had swept for nebulae especially attracted her wrath. Visitors would tell her of "... Lord Queenstown's great telescope, which shall beat Sir William Herschel's all to nothing, and such a visit sometimes makes me merry for a whole day".[154] Two years later she reported that "They talk of nothing here at the clubs but of the great mirror and the great man who made it". Caroline's response was less than polite: "I have but one answer for all, which is, 'Der Kerl ist ein Narr!' ['That guy is a jerk!'] ...."[155]

As late as 1845, she was still at work on her (second) autobiography, writing of events that took place sixty or seventy years before, with a firm, clear hand and a memory undimmed. But thereafter she falls silent, and it is to one of Dietrich's daughters that we owe an insight into her troubled state as she approached her death on 9 January 1848. Writing to John a few days later to tell him the news, Anna Knipping admits

> ... I felt almost a sense of joyful relief at the death of my aunt, in the thought that now the unquiet heart was at rest. All that she had of love to give was concentrated on her beloved brother. At his death she felt herself alone. For after those long years of separation she could not but find us all strange to her, and no one could ever replace his loss. Time did indeed lessen and soften the overpowering weight of her grief, and then she would regret that she had ever left England, and condemned herself to live in a country where nobody cared for astronomy. I shared her regret, but I knew too well that even in England she must have found the same blank. She looked upon progress in science as so much detraction from her brother's fame, and even your investigations would have become a source of estrangement had she been with you. She lived altogether in the past, and she found the present not only strange but annoying....[156]

Frantz Johann

Frantz Johann, the ninth of Isaac and Anna's children, was born on 13 May 1752, and died on 26 March 1754.[1] Caroline records that he succumbed to smallpox, and that she contracted the disease at the same time, which left her disfigured.[2]

Dietrich

Johann Dietrich, youngest of the ten children born to Isaac and Anna, could hardly have chosen a less auspicious time for his entry into the world. His birth on 13 September 1755 was quickly followed by an end to the period of peace during which Isaac had been able to live at home with his family. For most of the boy's infancy his father was absent with his regiment, and only in May 1760 did Isaac obtain his dismission from the army and return to his family, broken in health. Almost his first act after their reunion was to string a miniature violin and begin to teach his four-year-old son. Within weeks the child was displaying the Herschel talent for music, and at a public concert, "before a crouded company", Dietrich was hoisted onto a table between the acts so that he could play a solo on his little violin, accompanied by his father on a bass viol. An English lady put a gold coin in his pocket, and this Dietrich invested in skates, humming tops and fur gloves.[1]

In the seven years that remained to him, Isaac did all he could to advance Dietrich's musical training, and on his deathbed early in 1767 he committed this obligation to his eldest son Jacob.[2] But before many weeks had passed, Jacob had decided to pay an extended and no doubt profitable visit to William in Bath, leaving Dietrich's musical education in the hands of Alexander. But even Jacob had a conscience of sorts, and the following summer he summoned Dietrich to Bath.[3]

Their mother appreciated the advantages to Dietrich of being with his two eldest brothers, both established musicians; but she was dismayed at the thought that her twelve-year-old boy should be exposed to the temptations of the wider world before he had been fortified by the rite of Confirmation, which was normally administered at the age of fourteen. The brothers assured her that this would be taken care of on Dietrich's arrival in Bath, and so Anna arranged for the boy to accompany two surgeons who were travelling to England.[4]

Anna was illiterate but had children who could write letters for her, and before long she was demanding to know when the Confirmation was to take place. She found the replies far from convincing, and at length insisted that Dietrich return to Hanover. In July 1769 he duly arrived with Jacob as escort, and resumed attendance at the Garrison School. The following Easter, being aged fourteen, he was confirmed, and left school to devote himself to his profession of music.[5]

Within a few weeks, however, Jacob was off again to Bath, this time with Alexander who had two years' leave from the Court Orchestra.

> Meanwhile Dieterich (his Mother's Pet) was spending his time among boys of his own age ad libitum; and his practising would have been totally neglected, if several Scholars of Alexander … had not coaxed him to continue the Lessens with him till Alexanders return.[6]

Alexander in fact would choose to settle permanently in Bath, and such was Dietrich's musical ability that although he was barely fifteen, he deputized for Alexander in the Court Orchestra "and played in general as a supernumerary who was to fill the next vacancy that should offer".[7]

In the summer of 1772, Caroline too departed for Bath, and for five years we hear no more of Dietrich. He re-enters Caroline's autobiographies in dramatic fashion in July 1777. Then nearly twenty-two years old, and the holder of an enviable position in the Court Orchestra, the young man took it into his head to flee Hanover in secret with a companion of his own age, with the intention of taking ship for the East Indies. Anna's letter to Bath appealing for help met with an instant response. William immediately dropped what he was doing and took the afternoon coach to London, where he was relieved to learn that no ship had recently left for the East Indies and so Dietrich must still be within reach. He decided to continue to Hanover, where he discovered that the runaways had got cold feet, and that Dietrich's companion had returned home, leaving Dietrich to continue to England. William assumed that by then his brother would have reached Bath.[8]

In fact Caroline had had as yet no word of him, but before long a letter arrived from London to say that Dietrich was lying ill at an inn near the Tower. Alexander was currently in nearby Bristol; but next day he was to walk over to see his sister. That morning, Caroline set out to meet him with the alarming news, on hearing which Alexander took a hurried breakfast, ordered horses, and set out for London, arriving at Dietrich's bedside the following day. After two weeks of loving care and attention the miscreant was well enough to journey by stages to Bath, where Caroline on doctor's orders fed him a diet of roasted apples and barley water — until William arrived home and robustly ordered Dietrich to the family table.[9]

When we consider the huge amount of trouble and expense that Dietrich had caused by his escapade, the absence of any hint of reproach on the part of either William, Caroline or Alexander is remarkable. Perhaps they understood all too well what living with Anna could involve, for the possibility of despatching Dietrich back to his outraged mother (and to his post in the Court Orchestra) seems not to have been considered: "My brother D. [writes Caroline] remained with us two years, his Brother [William] recommended him to some Scholars and the Playhouse business &c. which made his stay with us very profitable to him."[10] William's "Memorandums" flesh this out:

> 1778. Jan. My brother John Dietrich attended Lord Abbington and other scholars. We had weekly concerts at Bristol; at the Lower Rooms at Bath, and also at the New Rooms, all of which John Diet. attended.
>
> Jan. 21st. I received 10 guineas for 10 concerts and for the same, 5 guineas for John Diet.
>
> March. 4 concerts a month; 4 guin; John Diet. for the same 4 guin. He played the principal 2nd violin.

It was profitable also to William, but in quite a different way. The intellectual curiosity instilled in his sons by Isaac had led Dietrich to interest himself in entomology, and during his stay in England he involved William in his passion for collecting butterflies. Indeed, William proved a willing pupil, for after Dietrich returned to Hanover in the summer of 1779 William continued to send him specimens. This served little purpose because in Germany such butterflies were common; but Dietrich was intrigued to know how William had preserved them.[11] Thus did William encounter the methodology of the natural historian, which he was soon to introduce into astronomy with the most dramatic consequences.

Dietrich's enthusiasm for natural history was to prove no passing whim, for William later describes him as "an eminent Musician, and well known as a scientific member of several Academies",[12] and he was to publish at least one catalogue of insects.[13] William for his part introduced Dietrich to astronomy: William's record of work on specula shows that on 27 April 1779 he repolished the mirror of Dietrich's 3-ft Gregorian reflector,[14] and Dietrich's interest in observing persisted, for when he was back in Hanover he wrote to ask William to repolish his mirror once more.[15] In 1786, when Caroline found her first comet, she wrote a long letter to Dietrich "as you have an instrument", explaining exactly where it was to be found ("I believe you have a pair of Harris's maps") and detailing the telescope she had used, in the expectation that his interest in astronomy was serious enough for him to search for the comet.[16]

Soon after his return to Hanover, on 5 October 1779, Dietrich married the nineteen-year-old Catharina Maria Reiff in the Garrison Church that had so many family associations for the Herschels. Catharina was the second daughter of the family's landlord (and Court musician[17]), Georg Heinrich Reiff, and his wife Anna Elizabeth.[18]

Dietrich then settled down to the regular routine of a Court musician. The couple were to have four children: Georg Heinrich, born on 7 March 1781; Anna Elisabeth, on 17 June 1783; Sophia Dorothea, on 3 June 1785; and Caroline Wilhelmine Marie Antonie, on 10 June 1799.[19] All were baptized in the Garrison Church.

In the autumn of 1782, when news of William's move to Windsor reached his family in Hanover, it was Dietrich who wrote to William about the plan that he and Jacob were hatching to secure Alexander's return to Hanover, for "we want to know what poor Alex is doing alone in Bath".[20] When William visited Hanover in July 1786, he found that "John [i.e. Dietrich] is just the same as before. his little boy [Heinrich] seems to be a charming creature".[21] Six years later Dietrich must have written to William to tell him of the murder by strangulation of their brother Jacob. In a second letter, Dietrich reported on Jacob's estate which, as Jacob had been unmarried, was to be divided among the family. But William — now a wealthy married man — declined his share, and Dietrich gratefully accepted it, viewing it as a gift from his brother.[22] "I know that you love giving," he wrote on another occasion, "and do it in such a way that it is impossible to refuse, so nothing remains but to say how sincerely I thank you".[23]

On the death of Sophia in 1803, Dietrich became the only one of the Herschel siblings still resident in Hanover. On 30 July of the previous year his eldest daughter Anna had married a merchant named Christian Philipp Knipping who was German but had spent time in the USA,[24] and the couple were living in Bremen.[25] Dietrich had consulted William about a possible post in the East India Company for his son Heinrich,[26] but the boy accepted instead a position with a client of Knipping's in Charlestown, just outside Boston. Before long he died there, of yellow fever.[27] His father's loss is reflected in the letter Dietrich wrote to William in March 1806 announcing his intention to visit England later that year, one that reveals his warm and affectionate nature. William's son John was now the only one left to carry on the family name. "I long to see good old Alexander, and Caroline who is so kind to us; and to see your son would alone be worth the journey: he will soon be the only one of our race."[28] Dietrich arrived on 6 July, and left on the 24th.[29]

He was soon to return, but in less happy circumstances. Hanover had become a pawn in the power struggle between Napoleon and the King of Prussia, and in July 1808 Caroline records that "We received very distressing accounts from our brother in Hanover".[30] Eventually Dietrich decided that the only way he could support his family was to go to England, ply his trade there as a musician, and send money home. He arrived in November 1808, and stayed until the summer of 1812. They were difficult times for Caroline: "From the hour of Dietrich's arrival in England till that of his departure, which was not till nearly four years after, I had not a day's respite from accumulated trouble and anxiety, for he came ruined in health, spirit, and fortune...."[31]

In 1803 Caroline had agreed to accept £10 a quarter from William's wife Mary as a supplement to her pension from the King, and during Dietrich's stay in England she made this money over to him.[32] The bond between her and her baby brother was close: "my whole life almost has passed away in the delusion that next to my eldest brother [William], none but Dietrich was capable of giving me advice."[33] Indeed, in some ways Dietrich was the closest of her siblings, for in William's later years she "kept to the resolution of never opening my lips to my dear brother William about worldly or serious concerns".[34]

As William grew old and infirm, Caroline pondered the problem of what she should do when he passed away. In 1820 she took a fateful decision. In Hanover, Alexander was enjoying his retirement, and Dietrich was there with his family, by all accounts "noble-hearted and perfect beings".[35] She therefore sent him £30 with which to buy her a feather bed.[36] The die was cast.

Alexander died the following year, but Dietrich and his extended family were there to welcome Caroline. They had more than their share of problems. As William's life neared its end, Caroline received "very distressing accounts of family misfortunes from my brother in Hanover".[37] On 2 July 1822, Dietrich's eldest daughter Anna was widowed only a few days after the birth of her ninth child.[38] Meanwhile the husband of his second daughter Dorothea, Dr Johann Richter, had become deranged, so much so that in the years to come Dietrich would be obliged to remove Dorothea and her four children to safety.[39] Moved by this, and glad as ever to help, Caroline made over to Dietrich her life savings of £500.[40]

When William died on 25 August 1822, his son John wrote to Dietrich concerning "My aunt's fixed determination to quit England" for Hanover, and to ask him in due course to send news of her safe arrival. Dietrich, to his immense credit, would not allow Caroline to undertake the journey alone. He himself was just recovering from a serious illness, and journeying the 70km between Hanover and Anna's home at Lachem to offer what help he could had been too much for his weak constitution. Yet despite all this he travelled to England to fetch his sister.[41]

The return crossing was stormy. But when they reached haven at last, Caroline found reason to wonder if perhaps she had made a terrible mistake:

> But in the last hope of finding in Dietrich a brother to whom I might communicate all my thoughts of past, present, and future, I saw myself disappointed the very first day of our travelling on land. For let me touch on what topic I would, he maintained the contrary, which I soon saw was done merely because he would allow no one to know anything but himself.[42]

She particularly resented Dietrich's complaints about what he saw as the poor education his father had given him: he "forever murmured at having received too scanty an education, though he had the same schooling we all of us had before him".[43] However, his wife's reception of Caroline was "truly gratifying", and rooms "have been prepared for me and furnished in the most elegant style".

Caroline found herself part of a large extended family that included Dietrich's three daughters: the widowed Anna Knipping and her nine children; Dorothea Richter and her four children, whose physician father was able to practise only in the intervals when his sanity was restored;[44] and Caroline, the youngest, married to Dr Groskopff, who was elderly but prosperous and by whom she had a son.[45] Caroline Herschel was later to name Groskopff as her executor,[46] but it was Anna who became her loyal and much loved friend, and who would one day write to John with news of his aunt's death.

Meanwhile Caroline was increasingly concerned about the well-being of Dietrich, whose companionship had been a prime motive for her return to Hanover. A decade earlier Dietrich had been resident in England, and one would think that Caroline had had ample opportunity to judge whether his company was congenial or not. No doubt, in the interval, his poor health and family cares had soured his normally affectionate nature.[47] Caroline maintained peace between them by holding her tongue: "... to combat against infirmities and peevishness (the usual companions of old age) depends entirely on my exertion to bear the same without communication, for unfortunately we are never in the same mind."[48] Her letters speak constantly of her brother's ill-health. In August 1826, for example, "his health is so very precarious, that I often think he will go before me".[49] By the beginning of November he had improved a little: "My Brother has recovered so far that he has taken a walk once or twice and is now as well as he was 5 or 6 months ago, but he wants as much nursing as a man 20 years older than what he is."[50] Sympathy from Caroline was hard-earned: "I hardly ever knew a man of his age labouring under more infirmities, nor bearing them with less patience than he does."[51]

Perhaps Dietrich was deserving of better than this, for at 1.30 a.m. on 19 January he died.[52]

The Herschelian Revolution
in Astronomy

William Herschel, perhaps alone in the history of astronomy, excelled as instrument-maker, as dedicated observer, and as innovative theoretician. His theories were based on the data assembled in his observational campaigns, in which the assistance of Caroline was invaluable; and these campaigns exploited the excellence of telescopes he had designed and which he made himself, either alone or with the help of Alexander or of teams of workmen acting under William's supervision.

"ONE OF THE GREATEST MECHANICS OF HIS DAY"[1]

There were a number of components that went to make up any of the reflectors that William built: the tube and stand, the eyepieces (with different magnifications to meet different needs), and above all the mirrors.[2] Grinding a mirror into the parabolic shape that was theoretically ideal, and then polishing it so that it reflected as much as possible of the light that fell upon it, was as much an art as a craft. The mirror of 7 feet focal length he made in Bath in May 1776 and used in his early 'reviews' was, it turned out, a masterpiece of the art, of "extraordinary excellence" in the words of the Astronomer Royal,[3] certainly the finest of its kind in England. This had far-reaching implications: many of William's double stars — the Pole Star, for example — appeared single in rival telescopes, so that his catalogues of doubles were truly impressive additions to the literature; and without such a fine mirror he would have seen Uranus as an ordinary star, as did Nevil Maskelyne at Greenwich Observatory and Thomas Hornsby at Oxford University. In short, had he not perfected this 7-ft mirror, it is unlikely he would have become a professional astronomer. Even he was not able to replicate its excellence when he supplied a similar 7-ft reflector to Greenwich.[4]

William's 7-ft was a precision instrument for the examination of nearby planets and stars. For the study of distant and therefore faint objects such as nebulae, the primary requirement was for a large mirror that would collect as much light as possible from the object and so bring it into view. Of the major reflectors that William made for his own use, the first later became known as the 'small' 20-ft. Built in 1778, it had mirrors 12 inches in diameter, which was a respectable size, but the tube was merely slung from a pole, and the observer was perched precariously in the dark, on a ladder that itself must have approached 20-ft in height. His attempts in 1781 to cast an ambitious mirror 3 feet in diamter had come to naught. It was

The 7-ft reflector with which William discovered Uranus and which he used in his early "reviews" which resulted in his two catalogues of double stars. From a drawing by William Watson, RAS W.5/5, no. 3.

time to take a more modest step forward, and to make suitable provision for the convenience and safety of the observer.

The result was a reflector that William would use to great effect in exploring 'the construction of the heavens'. The 'large' 20-ft came into service in October 1783, a year after his arrival at Datchet. Its mirrors were 18 inches in diameter, and so had more than twice the surface area of those of the 'small' 20-ft. It was mounted within a stable, ladder-work structure. When William needed to track an object for some minutes as the sky wheeled overhead, he stood on a platform with a handrail for safety and slowly pulled the tube from one side to the other. But if current work required the telescope to face exactly south, in the manner of a transit instrument, then William might prefer the more manageable observing chair.[5]

The monster 40-ft reflector with mirrors 4 feet in diameter that William completed in the late 1780s was, as we have seen, a major disappointment and

The reflector of 2-ft aperture and 10-ft focal length, which William built in 1799 as a manageable instrument for his declining years. RAS W.5/5, no. 12.

contributed little to his scientific work. Altogether more successful were the 25-ft with 2-ft mirrors that he made for the King of Spain around the turn of the century,[6] and the 10-ft reflector with 2-ft mirrors that he completed for his own use in 1799.[7] The 10-ft represented a modest but worthwhile increase in 'light gathering power' as compared with the 'large' 20-ft, but its greatest merit was to have a mounting so convenient that "I can get any object in less than half a minute"[8] — and William no longer had the agility of youth. To grind the parabolic shape necessary for a large mirror with a focal length of only 10 feet presented a challenge, but one that William was now experienced enough to meet. He made good use of the instrument during his sixties and early seventies, but in 1814 he sold it to Lucien Bonaparte.[9]

"UNSER NEUE GALILEI"[10]

Just as William was one of the great telescope builders of all time, so he was one of the greatest of observers. By assembling data on stars and other objects in what we now speak of as 'deep space', he began the process whereby the focus of astronomers' interest gradually shifted from the nearby Sun and planets to the stellar universe and even the cosmos as a whole.

William conducted four major observing campaigns. The earliest comprised his second and third "reviews" of the brighter stars with the 7-ft reflector (his first review — an examination of the stars down to fourth magnitude — was barely worthy of the name).[11] The second review, which extended to stars invisible to the naked eye, he began on 17 August 1779. Not only did it serve to familiarize him with the night sky, but it had a theoretical purpose: the accumulation of specimens of double stars, some of which might serve for the determination of stellar distances. It resulted in the catalogue of 269 double stars that he sent to the Royal Society at the end of 1781,[12] as well as in the discovery of Uranus. Late in 1784 he sent the Royal Society a catalogue of a further 434 doubles, the fruit of his third review, which had been more extensive and conducted with a higher magnification.[13]

These catalogues were perhaps the first in astronomy to be organized according to the methods of the natural historian. His brother Dietrich had lodged with him for the two years immediately prior to his second review. Dietrich was an enthusiastic entomologist, and he taught William how to collect specimens: William was a natural historian of butterflies before he became a natural historian of double stars. The double stars he had collected, he classified according to the degree of separation between the two components, and listed by the date of discovery.

His second and greatest observing campaign took the form of a twenty-year

William's sketch of the Orion Nebula made on 4 March 1774, RAS W.2/1.1, f. 1.

search for nebulae and star clusters. Back in 1774, when he had opened his first "Journal", William had sketched the Orion Nebula. When he compared this sketch with that reproduced in Robert Smith's *Opticks*, he decided the nebula had meanwhile altered shape. During the next five years he observed the Orion Nebula seven more times and sketched it twice, and on 15 December 1778 he again thought he had evidence of change: "But there is a visible alteration in the figure of the lucid part."[14] If so, it could not be a distant, and therefore vast, star system, for distant stars would not be able to rearrange themselves so rapidly.

Between the autumn of 1779 and December 1781, when William Watson presented him with the second of the catalogues of nebulae and clusters assembled by the French comet-hunter Charles Messier, William observed three more nebulae: the globular cluster M 13, which he thought "a nebula without stars in it"; the galactic cluster M 11; and the Andromeda Nebula, M 31 ("Has no star in it"; "no star visible").[15] His 'small' 20-ft with its 12-inch mirrors was an instrument capable of showing all of Messier's objects, but the arrival of the catalogue did not immediately stimulate his interest in nebulae: even in his first months as a professional astronomer he was still preoccupied with the search for double stars (although he did take an early opportunity to show M 11 and M 31 to the King[16]). Caroline, however, no longer had a career as a singer to pursue, and so (William supposed) she had time on her hands. He therefore provided her with a primitive refractor and told her to look out for, among other things, nebulae and clusters of stars.[17]

As one would expect, all the examples of these mysterious objects that she encountered in her first weeks of observation were already known to Messier, whose third and final catalogue of a hundred or so such objects, which are cometlike in appearance but in fact permanent, we still use today. But on 26 February 1783 Caroline came across two clusters concerning each of which she and William were agreed that "Messier has it not".

They were mistaken: the first of Caroline's two clusters was in fact M 93, and only the second was a new discovery. But the impression William took away from the night's viewing was that nebulae and clusters were so numerous that even an inexperienced observer, using a telescope that was little more than a toy, could find examples unknown to astronomy. A week later, on 4 March, he decided himself "to sweep the heaven for Nebulas and Clusters of stars".[18]

The 'large' 20-ft was some months away from completion, and in his impatience William began to search with "the 3½ft achromatic with a single eye-lens". But soon the absurdity of using a small telescope to search for faint and permanent objects in the night sky struck him, and so he concentrated during the summer months on familiarizing himself with the prominent nebulae listed by Messier.

The 20-ft first saw light on 23 October 1783 and on the 28th William began to sweep. The instrument was at first fixed in the meridian, facing south but with the tube moveable a few degrees to one side or the other. The method he adopted was cumbersome in the extreme. After dragging the tube from one side to the other, manhandling it from the observing platform through a range in azimuth (horizontal angle) of up to 30°, and noting anything of interest, he would raise or lower the tube by some 8' or 10' and do the same again; ten or twenty such passes were deemed to constitute a sweep.[19]

Within a few weeks he had to accept that this method of sweeping would not do. To make written notes he had to use artificial light, and it would then be some minutes before his eyes were once more dark-adjusted and able to detect faint nebulae. Not only that, but the manhandling of the tube was an exhausting business, for it was suspended by ropes from a central position and so had to be lifted a little when dragged to one side or other. His 45 sweeps had yielded no more than eight nebulae.

The answer clearly lay in teamwork. In future the tube would normally be kept positioned exactly in the meridian, in the manner of transit instruments, and William would study the sky as it drifted across his field of view. Because the Earth spins slowly, he found that he had time to examine a much broader band of sky than was visible at any one moment in the field of view of the 20-ft, and therefore he decided to employ a workman who would raise and lower the tube in regular fashion. Experience showed that near the celestial equator, where the apparent movement of the celestial sphere was most rapid, there was time for him to search a band of sky some 2° wide. Near the North Pole, the width could approach 5°.

To record his observations, and to keep track of the identities of the brighter stars he was encountering (and by reference to which the positions of nebulae would be established), William needed the help of Caroline, who would be seated at a desk at a nearby window ready to copy down whatever her brother shouted out.

In the early months of sweeping, William gave this enterprise priority among the various claims on his time. There were nights when clouds or moonlight prevented him from observing, but despite this, in the calendar year of 1784 he and Caroline netted nebulae on no fewer than 95 nights; and by 26 April 1785 the number in the bag had risen to one thousand, a convenient number for their first catalogue.[20]

In the later 1780s, William was compelled to devote much of his energies to directing the army of workmen engaged in the construction of the 40-ft. Nevertheless, at night the sweeps continued. In 1785, he and Caroline netted 581 nebulae; in 1786, 318; and in 1787, 247. In 1788 the number of nebulae dropped to 160; and that year there emerged a new and enduring rival to night watches at the telescope, the attractions of William's newly-acquired wife.

By early December 1788 the second thousand nebulae were in the bag.[21] The first thousand — or more exactly, 991, for nine were known before collaborative sweeping began — had taken them sixteen months; the second thousand, over forty-three. After the glory years of 1783 and 1784, the annual crop of nebulae had dropped first to half, and then to less than a quarter.

A considerable area of sky remained to be swept, but William no longer found the work appealing. He had developed other research interests that called for time at the 20-ft. More importantly, an observation he made in November 1790 (of a star surrounded by a halo of nebulosity, see below) convinced him that not all nebulae were star clusters, and this settled the theoretical issue that underlay the programme of sweeps. In 1791 he swept on only twenty nights, in 1792 on nine, in 1793 on twenty-three, and in 1794 on seven. The final sweep of 1794 took place on 18 October, and thereafter the campaign was all but abandoned: for three years not a single sweep was undertaken, the only nebula netted being a chance success during observations of satellites of Uranus.[22] A further difficulty then arose, for in October 1797 Caroline made the extraordinary decision to move out of her cottage in the grounds of William's house and go into lodgings.[23] No longer would she be on hand at night whenever the skies cleared and her help was needed. Instead, her presence must be pre-planned; and when the night's work was over she must be escorted back to her lodgings.

This must have focused William's mind on the problem of what to do about future sweeps, and about the publication of the 428 nebulae they had accumulated since the last catalogue was published. In addition to a few unswept patches of sky that transited south of the zenith, extensive areas to the north had thus far been neglected. It would have been well within the bounds of possibility to sweep all the remaining areas, and so fulfil the promise made long ago to continue "till the whole be completed".[24] A more modest ambition would have been to raise the total of 428, not of course to the one thousand of former catalogues — such a total was out of the question as the area of unswept sky was now limited — but to half that number.

And this, it seems, was the decision, though not one carried out with any enthusiasm. William and Caroline made a few sweeps in the remaining weeks of 1797, and then none until September of 1798. In the whole of 1799 they swept on a mere four nights, and in 1800 on only one single night. At long last, after eleven nights in 1801 and four in the first half of 1802, the magic total of 500 was (they thought) reached, and another catalogue could be sent to the Royal Society for publication.[25] Caroline's manuscript was dated 29 June 1802,[26] and it was formally read to the Society two days later.

Several regions still remained unswept, most of which were north of the zenith; but William had long since lost his enthusiasm. His family demanded attention. On 13 July he set off for Paris, and did not return until 25 August.[27]

Within a month, he and Caroline had realized that by oversight the catalogue comprised, not 500 nebulae, but 497. There was nothing for it but to go out and find three more. On 25 September he and Caroline swept again, but without success. On the 26th they had better luck and netted six nebulae: three to make up the present catalogue to 500, and three for the next catalogue. It seems they retrieved the manuscript from the Royal Society, to allow Caroline to insert the three additions.

On the 30th they swept again and found another four: they now had seven nebulae towards the next catalogue. But soon, it seems, the proofs of the catalogue of 500 nebulae arrived, and William evidently had a change of heart. He was now well into his sixties, and the winters were far more severe than today. If he and his sister had applied themselves to the task, another year would have brought a conclusion to the great enterprise, to sweep for nebulae over the whole of the skies accessible to them. But to what end? Perhaps another hundred nebulae to add to the 2,500 already in the bag? Why bother? And so William decided to call a halt. No change was made to either the "five hundred" of the title of the catalogue now in proof or the prefatory remarks. Instead, and misleadingly, the seven additional nebulae were quietly inserted into the proofs,[28] along with three from earlier years that had been overlooked,[29] to bring the total to 510; while readers were left with the impression that the catalogue was of exactly 500 nebulae and part of what was still an ongoing series. Publicly, therefore, nothing was said; but sweeping was abandoned, and the great enterprise left unfinished.

The third of William's observing campaigns came early in his professional career, and the data he assembled are featured in his 1784 and 1785 papers on 'the construction of the heavens'.[30] His "star-gages" — the numbers of stars visible in his telescope when it was pointed in various directions — became the pioneering exercise in stellar statistics, and (as we shall see) he showed how fruitful the mere counting of stars might prove to be.

The detection of variations in the brightnesses of stars was the object of William's fourth observing campaign.[31] Since Antiquity, stars had been spoken of as "fixed", *stellae fixae*, for (it seemed) they never changed their positions relative to each other or their apparent brightnesses, in contrast to the planets each of which moved as an individual and which were brighter at some times and less bright at others. By Newton's day it was recognized that the stars were in fact distant suns, free to move in infinite space, although when Newton published *Principia* in 1687 no single star was in fact known to have moved relative to other stars. Variations in brightness, however, were by now well-established. A brilliant new star had appeared in 1572 and another in 1604; and in addition, during the seventeenth century a number of other stars had been found to vary in brightness. Among them were o Ceti, known to go through a cycle every 333 or so days, and Algol (β Lyrae), normally a bright star of second magnitude but seen in 1667 and again in 1670 as only of fourth. Many other stars were alleged to vary; but it was proving impossible to distinguish genuine variables from the subjects of the numerous spurious claims in circulation. And so, for a time, interest in variables waned.

In the early 1780s two amateur observers, Edward Pigott and John Goodricke, who were neighbours in York in the north of England, took it upon themselves to revive the search for variables, and their efforts were rewarded late in 1782 when they saw Algol drop from second magnitude to fourth in a matter of hours, before their very eyes. Pigott suspected at first that the star was being eclipsed by a companion (as indeed it is). By mid-April of 1783 they had established the period of variation as under three days, a phenomenon hitherto unknown to astronomy. Pigott informed the Astronomer Royal, and asked him to pass word to William. He at once kept watch, and when on 8 May 1783 he went to London for a dinner and a meeting of the Royal Society, he was pressed by those present to report on his observations. Believing the variations to be public knowledge he gave an account of what he had seen, only to find that the planned paper by Goodricke had not yet been submitted and that he had inadvertently anticipated the York astronomers' formal announcement. Happily, after a delicate exchange of correspondence William's explanation was accepted, and there the matter rested.[32]

In their searches, which led in all to the identification of four short-period variables, Pigott and Goodricke had developed a method of detecting and confirming variations: they listed stars in extended sequences by order of brightness, in the hope that a variable star lurking within such a sequence would betray its variability by disturbing the established order. In the 1790s William decided to exploit this method on a large scale and to bequeath to later generations a data-base against which they could monitor alleged variations. This he did in the form of four vast catalogues "Of the Comparative Brightness of Stars", published in *Philosophical Transactions* between 1796 and 1799. A century later, a Harvard astronomer commented, "Herschel furnished observations of nearly 3000 stars, from which their magnitudes a hundred years ago can now be determined with an accuracy approaching that of the best modern catalogues.... The error of a single comparison but little exceeds a tenth of a magnitude".[33]

TRANSFORMING ASTRONOMY

To the seventeenth century, the clock of the cathedral at Strasbourg was a model in miniature of the universe itself.[34] Complex though the timepiece was, the operation of each component dial was simple and intelligible. Similarly, it was thought, the universe as a whole was complex in its totality but simple and intelligible in the detail of its mechanical operation. God was the great Clockmaker.

René Descartes imagined God as creating the matter of the universe, and setting it in motion, and then (so to speak) washing his hands of it — leaving the laws of mechanics to take their course. To Isaac Newton this smacked of atheism. In his view, Providence had what we might term a regular servicing contract with the universe. The solar system had been designed by Providence so that the disruptive elements — the massive planets Jupiter and Saturn — were at the outside where their pulls would do least harm. But in time these perturbations would accumulate, and then the system would "want a reformation": Providence would intervene to restore order. Newton also analysed counts of stars of the first, second, third, ... magnitudes to justify his belief that the nearer stars were distributed with near-uniformity. Extrapolating and taking this supposition to be well-founded for the infinite universe as a whole, Newton concluded that because each star was pulled almost equally in opposite directions by the stars to one side and to the other, it would in the short term remain more-or-less at rest. But the distribution was not perfectly uniform, and so in the longer term the system would be threatened with collapse; and then Providence would intervene to restore order.

Newton saw these interventions as part of the divine plan foreseen from the Creation; by recognizing this, mankind could learn about the love of God from the Book of Nature as well as from the Book of Revelation. The interventions were therefore not miracles, not 'emergency call-outs' of the divine Clockmaker, and so in no way a sign of incompetence on the part of the Creator.[35]

Gottfried Wilhelm Leibniz saw it differently:

> Sir Isaac Newton, and his followers, have also a very odd opinion concerning the work of God. According to their doctrine, God Almighty wants to wind up his watch from time to time: otherwise it would cease to move.... Nay, the machine of God's making, is so imperfect, according to these gentlemen; that he is obliged to clean it now and then by an extraordinary concourse, and even to mend it, as a clockmaker mends his work....[36]

The exchange of salvoes between Leibniz and Newton's spokesman, Samuel Clarke, ended, as so often is the case, with the death of one of the participants. But their dispute was over matters of detail: both sides were agreed that God was the great Clockmaker, and that in its fundamentals the universe was changeless, as a well-made clock is changeless.

Following in their footsteps, mathematical astronomers in the eighteenth century saw themselves as students of the recurring cyclic movements of the bodies of the solar system. The challenge facing them was to demonstrate that all of these movements could be accounted for by Newton's inverse-square law of gravitational attraction. Discussion of the cosmos as a whole was left to a handful of speculators who were outside the astronomical community and who had almost no impact on the science.[37]

The contrast with astronomy in our own day could scarcely be greater. Study of the solar system is today a minority pursuit, and most professionals are concerned with features of the larger-scale universe. Change is everywhere. Stellar evolution, for example, is defined by one textbook as "the progressive series of changes undergone by a star as it ages". Even the cosmos as a whole has a life-story, beginning with the Big Bang.

William did more than anyone to bring about this dramatic reorientation of astronomy. True, he made significant contributions to our knowledge of the solar system (which he was convinced was inhabited throughout[38]). His discovery of Uranus was sensational.[39] Six years later he found two of Uranus's satellites, now known as Oberon and Titania; went on to establish their periods, orbital planes and greatest distances from the planet; and inferred that the mass of Uranus was some 18 times greater than that of Earth. In 1797 he claimed to have discovered four more satellites of Uranus (but here it seems he was deceived).[40] He found the Saturnian satellites Enceladus and Mimas, and devoted so much attention to the planet that the standard history devotes two whole chapters to his work.[41] He measured the heights of mountains on the Moon, and spent time searching for evidence of volcanic activity: in 1787 he was convinced he had found his third active volcano (but although both he and Caroline continued to search in the following years, they saw no repetition of the phenomenon, whatever it was).[42]

But if William had not discovered Oberon and Titania, in due course some other observer would, and astronomy would have continued with little change. It is true that around half of William's papers in *Philosophical Transactions* deal with the solar system; but his epoch-making contributions to astronomy concerned the stars and 'the construction of the heavens'. To the sympathetic reader he demonstrated that, far from being an uninteresting backcloth to the motions of the planets, the stellar universe was a challenging and rewarding field of study, in which there were rich pickings for the intellectually adventurous.

William led by example. In the pages of *Philosophical Transactions*, no less, and when he had been a professional astronomer for under three years, he gave notice that he would rather theorize too much than too little:

> ... if we hope to make any progress in an investigation of this delicate nature, we ought to avoid two opposite extremes, of which I can hardly say which is the most dangerous. If we indulge a fanciful imagination and build worlds of our own, we must not wonder at our going wide from the path of truth and nature; but these will vanish like the Cartesian vortices, that soon gave way when better theories were offered. On the other hand, if we add observation to observation, without attempting to draw not only certain conclusions, but also conjectural views from them, we offend against the very end for which only observations ought to be made. I will endeavour to keep a proper medium; but if I should deviate from that, I could not wish to fall into the latter error.[43]

We now outline first William's studies of the nearby stars, which were accessible also to other astronomers, and then his investigations of 'the construction of the heavens', where the evidence was in large measure available to him alone.

Our Neighbours among the Stars

Traditionally, a 'fixed' star had a position and an apparent brightness, and perhaps a distinctive colour. William more than once used a prism to examine the spectrum of the light from a prominent star, but he could do nothing with the information.[44] As to variations in brightness, we have seen that he assembled catalogues that future generations might use to check whether a particular star had indeed varied as claimed. But he accepted the usual physical explanation of these variations, that the star had dark patches like huge sunspots, and that regular variations were the effect of the star's rotation, while irregular ones were the result of changes in the patches.[45] This model was flexible enough to account for almost any observed variations, and there was little more that could be done in the understanding of variations until the available evidence was enriched in the mid-nineteenth century by the development of spectroscopy.

The fixity or otherwise of the stars, however, was another matter. When Newton had been writing *Principia*, he had believed the stars to be isolated bodies free to move, and it was puzzling as to why they seemed to be motionless. A generation later, Edmond Halley identified the first three 'proper motions' of individual stars,[46] and more soon followed. But the Sun was itself a star, and so the solar system too might have its own motion, travelling through space in a certain direction. Given the list of proper motions as known in William's day (these are of course movements *as seen from Earth*), would it be possible for him to determine the 'solar apex' — the direction towards which the solar system is moving?

William had read in Ferguson that "If our Solar System changes its place with regard to absolute space, this must in process of time occasion an apparent change in the [angular] distances of the Stars from each other".[47] The pattern such changes would take had been explained by Tobias Mayer in a lecture in 1760: if you are walking through a wood, the trees you are approaching appear to move apart, to one side or the other, while those you are leaving appear to move together.[48] The challenge was to detect such a pattern among the known proper motions, one that would reflect the motion of the solar system through space. Any motions outside the pattern would doubtless be due to the particular stars concerned.

A star's proper motion (in seconds of arc per annum) is determined by comparing its present position with its position at some time in the past, and the problem in the mid-eighteenth century was that only recently had factors come to light that showed that the accuracy of such past measurements of position was much less than had been thought. With few exceptions, therefore, the tiny proper motions had to be measured over only a brief time-span of years, and so the resulting data were unreliable. Not surprisingly, Mayer failed to detect any pattern in the proper motions available to him.

The understanding of observational errors and how they affect the data was then in its infancy, and Mayer was at fault for taking at face-value supposed proper motions that were negligible in size. The French astronomer Jerôme de Lalande rejected many of Mayer's data for just this reason; but he considered twelve of the motions to be large enough — in one or other coordinate — to merit citation in a book he published in 1781, and these thus became available to William. Also known to William were the lists of seven reliable motions in right ascension (longitude) and two in declination (latitude) tucked away on page iv of Maskelyne's 1776 volume of *Astronomical Observations*. In total, this information was enough for William early in 1783 to send to the Royal Society a paper that proposed a solar apex. The paper was most uncharacteristic of him, for it in no way relied on his own observations, but on data that were published and freely available to all.

As he tells the story, William began with Maskelyne's lists. The sought-for pattern of motions in right ascension is simple enough: if the solar system is moving in a given direction, stars to the left (so to speak) will move further left, and those to the right further right, just like trees in a forest. William found that every one of Maskelyne's seven motions could be accounted for (or 'saved', as the Greeks used to put it) if the solar system was assumed to be moving towards a point anywhere within a certain band of sky. Having established this, he examined Mayer's data as reported by Lalande, and he found that most (though not quite all) of these motions could similarly be accounted for.

The motion of Aldebaran, however, was of particular interest. Lalande had listed the star because its stated motion in declination was big enough to be taken seriously. Perhaps injudiciously, he had also cited its stated motion in right ascension: a mere 3 seconds of arc spread over half a century, a wholly negligible quantity given the instrumental errors involved. Yet William gullibly took these 3 seconds at face value, and used their direction to halve the band of sky he had derived from Maskelyne's data.

The pattern in declination is altogether more complex and need not detain us. Suffice it to say that by studying the motions in declination and then combining the two results, William concluded that the solar system is moving in the direction of the star λ Herculis. This is astonishingly close to the direction accepted by astronomers today. Yet if Aldebaran's supposed motion of 3 seconds of arc had chanced to have been cited as being in the opposite direction, as well it might, William's direction would have been over 30° away.

In 1805 William returned to the problem of the solar apex, and by now there were more and better data on proper motions available. Unfortunately, ambitious as ever, he attempted this time to establish not only the direction of travel of the solar system but also its velocity; and the velocity could be inferred only from a knowledge of the velocities relative to us of nearby stars.[49] The available evidence however took the form of the proper (that is, angular) motions of a handful of stars, each of which lay in a given direction from Earth and had a given apparent brightness. To derive the velocity of a star at right angles to the line of sight (for he had no clue to its radial velocity), he needed to multiply its proper motion by its distance. But what was its distance? William was forced to assume that the stars are physically similar, for if so then brightness is a reliable index of distance. Unfortunately this is far from being the case, and so his arguments became convoluted and lacked the simplicity of his earlier determination of the apex. Not for the only time in his career, William had taken a step too far.

The assumption that the stars were physically similar had been used by Newton a century earlier to demonstrate for the first time the true order of magnitude of the distances separating us from the nearest stars. If Sirius, say, is a physical twin of the Sun and looks fainter only because of the greater distance at which it lies, then a comparison of their apparent brightnesses will yield a comparison of their distances. Using an ingenious procedure due to James Gregory, Newton had concluded that the Sun is about one million million times brighter than Sirius, and so Sirius is about one million times further than the Sun. In this way he established the enormity of the distances of the stars, and therefore how very difficult and delicate would be the direct measurement of 'annual parallax', the apparent movement of a star resulting from our orbit of the Sun.[50] William had seen his double stars as a way of overcoming this problem, the more distant of the pair being in effect a fixed point against which the observer could track the apparent annual movement of the nearer and so determine its distance from Earth.

But were double stars in fact chance alignments, as the method required? John Michell had argued — on grounds of probability, but nevertheless persuasively — that most of William's innumerable double stars must in fact be what we would call 'binaries': not pairs of stars that happen by chance to lie in almost the same direction from us although at different distances, but companions in space bound to each other, by an attractive force (or forces) that might one day be shown to be Newtonian gravitation.[51] Such binaries would be useless for the measurement of stellar distances, since the two components lay at the same distance from the observer on Earth; but the very existence of binaries would prove that attractive forces operated outside the confines of the solar system.

In 1802, when the programme of sweeps was at last terminated, William made time to re-examine some of his double stars, and he found that in a number of them the two components had indeed altered position relative to each other, in a way that showed they were companions in space, just as Michell had predicted.[52] A generation later, enough would be known of the orbits to enable his son John and other observers to show that some at least of these doubles were bound to each other by Newtonian gravitation.[53]

The Construction of the Heavens

William's investigation of the nearer stars played its part in lifting astronomers' eyes to what lay outside our planetary system, but from the start his heart had been set on understanding the large-scale universe. As he wrote in 1811, "A knowledge of the construction of the heavens has always been the ultimate object of my observations".[54] He had been an autodidact in astronomy, teaching himself about the heavens from a couple of books he had acquired, and fortunately it happened that what they had to say about nebulae aroused his curiosity: some of these milky patches were undoubtedly nothing more than distant star systems; but were others 'truly' nebulous?

It was only in the autumn of 1783, when he completed the 'large' 20-ft, that he was able to devote himself to the problem. William had recently reobserved many of the hundred or so nebulae and clusters catalogued by Messier, and he and Caroline had already discovered a handful more. One of these was an object in Aquarius which he had come across on 7 September 1782.[55] It seemed to have a disk like a planet but the faint light of a nebula, and so he termed it a 'planetary nebula'. More planetary nebulae were to follow. They puzzled William considerably, and many a visiting astronomer would be required to view one of them and give his opinion of it.[56]

Of greater immediate importance were the sketches he had made from time to time of the Orion Nebula.[57] These convinced William that the object was altering shape and therefore could not be a vast and distant star system. In other words, it was truly nebulous. But how then was one to distinguish 'true nebulae' from those that were simply star systems so distant that they could not be 'resolved' into their component stars by the most powerful telescopes built to date (but which were in principle 'resolvable')? William persuaded himself that he was seeing two kinds of nebulous appearance in his telescope: the milky nebulosity of a true nebula, and the irregular, 'mottled' nebulosity of a distant star system. And this was his position in May 1784 when, after only a few months of sweeping for nebulae, he sent to the Royal Society the first of his great cosmological papers, "Account of Some Observations Tending to Investigate the Construction of the Heavens". [58]

It concerned, he said, "the *interior construction* of the heavens, and its various *nebulous and sidereal strata* (to borrow a term from the natural historian)". He had examined a section of the Milky Way and found it to consist entirely of stars,

> ... but, as the dazzling brightness of glittering stars may easily mislead us so far as to estimate their number as greater than it really is, I endeavoured to ascertain this point by counting many fields....

Today, it is a commonplace that the counting of great numbers of celestial objects of a particular kind can sometimes shed light on a theory; but to a generation accustomed to thinking of astronomy as primarily the study of the planets and their satellites, each of which was a familiar individual with its own proper name, this was a complete novelty.

Like some mid-century speculators before him,[59] William had realized that the phenomenon of the Milky Way can be explained if we imagine ourselves immersed in a nebula that has the form of a layer or 'stratum' of stars: when we look out away from the stratum, we will see only a few nearby (and therefore bright) stars; but when we look about us within the stratum, we will see great numbers of stars near and far, and this will generate the appearance of milkiness around a great circle of the sky. William being William, he set himself to determine the shape of this stratum of which the Sun is a member. There was obviously no question of his being able to do this unless his telescope — the 'large' 20-ft — could penetrate to the borders in all directions, and so this was one assumption he was forced to make. The second assumption had little evidence to support it, but it was one that would allow him to arrive at an answer: namely, that within the borders of our stratum, the stars are distributed with a fair approximation to uniformity. For if this is the case, then if we point the telescope in a given direction and count the stars visible in the field of view, the number will directly relate to the distance from Earth to the border in that direction: the more stars, the further to the border.

In his second cosmological paper, "On the Construction of the Heavens",[60] sent to the Royal Society on New Year's Day 1785, William included a long table of what he termed "star-gages". Each gage was a count of stars in a given direction — or, more commonly, ten counts in similar directions, added and averaged — and this was then converted into a (relative) distance by means of a simple arithmetical formula. He had not had the observing time to spare to allow him do this over the whole sky, but his table presented the results for a great circle. Sure enough, where the circle intersected the Milky Way, the counts were very high, implying that the Milky Way extended far out into space.

William used these counts to prepare a diagram displaying a cross-section of our star system, and for much of the nineteenth century this diagram is to be found in textbooks and popularizations. This is odd, for William was to abandon both of his assumptions, and therefore the diagram that was based upon them.[61] He abandoned the assumption that his 20-ft could penetrate to the borders in all directions when he commissioned his 40-ft reflector and found that it revealed many stars invisible in the 20-ft. He abandoned the assumption that the stars are distributed with fair uniformity when his many years of sweeping for nebulae and star clusters forced him finally to accept that the distribution of the stars was very far from regular, and that a high count was primarily an indication of clustering in the given direction. But he had nothing to offer in place of the diagram. Nevertheless, textbook writers, like Nature, abhor a vacuum, and the diagram continued to be published long after its author had disowned it.

Understandably, much of the 1784 paper was devoted to evidence of the power of his two 20-ft reflectors as tools for investigating the cosmos, and so he proudly lists Messier nebulae that he has been able to resolve into stars, and others that in his 'large' 20-ft are seen to be much more extensive than hitherto thought. Indeed, in the paper there is so much talk of resolutions that it is easy to forget that William then believed that there were nevertheless many true nebulae, which never would and never could be resolved into stars.

As is the way of things, soon after he despatched the 1784 paper to the Royal Society he came across two nebulae that forced him into a radical rethink. On 22 June 1784, just five days after the paper was read to the Society, William came across M 17, the so-called Omega Nebula. In it, he thought he detected both milky and mottled nebulosity:

> Should this be confirmed on a very fine night, it would bring on the step between these two nebulosities which is at present wanting, and would lead us to surmise that this nebula is a stupendous Stratum of immensely distant fixed stars some of whose branches are near enough to be visible as resolvable nebulosity, while the rest runs on to so great a distance as only to appear under the milky form.[62]

In other words, the difference between the two forms of nebulosity was not one of kind, as he had hitherto thought, but merely of distance: the parts of the stratum of stars nearest to us appeared mottled, while those further away appeared milky. Confirmation (as he thought) came a month later, when he examined M 27, the Dumbbell Nebula. This, he writes,

I suppose to be a double stratum of stars of a very great extent. The ends next to us are not only resolvable nebulosity but I really do see very many of the stars mixt with the resolvable nebulosity. Farther on the nebulosity is but rarely resolvable & ends at last in milky whitishness of the same appearance as that in [the nebula of] Orion.[63]

Again the (double) stratum stretched away from the observer, but this time William believed he could manage to detect, nearest to us, some of the individual stars. Further away, the stratum appeared mottled; and further still, milky.

The implications were profound. He had (it seemed) been too hasty in accepting there had been changes in the Orion Nebula, from the evidence of the primitive sketches he had made in his apprenticeship as an observer — changes that (if authentic) would imply that the nebula was near at hand and formed of 'true' nebulosity. In fact, he now believed, all nebulae were clusters of stars: some were near enough to be resolved by the 'large' 20-ft into the component stars; others were further away and appeared mottled; others were very distant and appeared milky. That was all there was to it.

The simplicity of this concept made it easy for William to see the implication: it must be that stars find themselves in a cluster because one or more attractive forces (perhaps gravitation as claimed by Newton) are at work; stars that once were widely-separated have pulled each other ever closer and so formed the cluster. But this process is surely set to continue, and the stars of a scattered cluster will go on pulling each other and so make the cluster ever more tightly-packed. The implication was as profound as any in the entire history of astronomy and it is impossible to exaggerate its significance: scattered clusters are young, tightly-packed clusters are old. It would be many years before astronomers as a whole accepted this insight and made it part of their thinking, but William had rung the death-knell of the clockwork universe and ushered in the universe of modern astronomy where everything, even the universe itself, has a life-history.

William encapsulates this theoretical transformation in the first paragraphs of his 1785 paper, where he writes: "Let us then suppose numberless stars of various sizes, scattered over an indefinite portion of space in such a manner as to be almost equally distributed throughout the whole." His reasoning is astonishingly similar to Newton's a century earlier. One of the "circumstances that do manifestly tend to a general preservation" is "the indefinite extent of the sidereal heavens, which must produced a balance that will effectually secure all the great parts of the whole from approaching to each other". In rotating star clusters, "projectile [that is, orbital] forces ... will prove such a barrier against the seeming destructive power of attraction" as to preserve the stars "if not for ever, at least for millions of ages". More generally, "there is no doubt but that the great Author of [the universe] has amply provided for the preservation of the whole, though it should not appear to us in what manner this is effected". Nevertheless, he believes that attraction is not merely a potential, but an actual agent of change. Where there

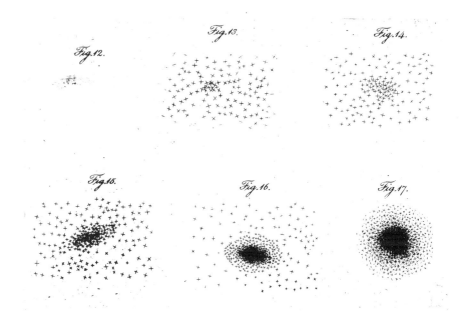

William's conception of how star clusters increasingly condense over time under the action of gravity. These diagrams come from his 1814 paper on "the sidereal part of the heavens", but he arrived at this conception in the 1780s.

is an unusually large star, or where the stars are unusually numerous, the force of attraction will be strong enough to pull in neighbouring stars, leaving empty spaces behind. But William shrinks from the obvious implication, that it is only a matter of time before the universe of stars falls victim to gravitational collapse on an ever-increasing scale. He is optimistic about a renewal of the universe, even if at the moment he does not understand how this will be achieved. Clusters in which there occurs "the destruction of now and then a star, in some thousands of ages … may be the *Laboratories* of the universe, if I may so express myself, wherein the most salutary remedies for the decay of the whole are prepared".

He then examines the structure of our own star system, and, as we have seen, uses gages to explore its shape. It is, he concludes, "A very extensive, branching, compound Congeries of many millions of stars". But it is finite, and other nebulae — that is, other star systems — "may well outvie our milky-way in grandeur". The Orion Nebula and the Andromeda Nebula, which extended across the sky yet were so distant that the 'large' 20-ft was not able to resolve them into their component stars, are examples of this.

On 1 May 1789 he sent to the Royal Society his third (and for the time being, last) cosmological paper, "Remarks on the Construction of the Heavens".[64] In it he hammered home the implications of his earlier papers. Convinced that all nebulae were star clusters and that the attraction that had produced the clustering was still at work, he insisted on the degree of clustering as an index of where the cluster was in its cycle of development. A cluster that was "very gradually more compressed and bright towards the middle, may be in the perfection of its growth, when another which approaches to the condition pointed out by a more equal compression, such as the nebulae I have called *Planetary* seem to present us with, may be looked upon as very aged, and drawing on towards a period of change, or dissolution". He ended with one of the noblest passages in the history of astronomy:

> This method of viewing the heavens seems to throw them into a new kind of light. They now are seen to resemble a luxuriant garden, which contains the greatest variety of productions, in different flourishing beds; and one advantage we may at least reap from it is, that we can, as it were, extend the range of our experience to an immense duration. For, to continue the simile I have borrowed from the vegetable kingdom, is it not almost the same thing, whether we live successively to witness the germination, blooming, foliage, fecundity, fading, withering, and corruption of a plant, or whether a vast number of specimens, selected from every stage through which the plant passes in the course of its existence, be brought at once to our view?[65]

Yet this elegant cosmogony was not without its problems. William was not entirely at ease with his view of the Orion Nebula as a very distant star system: it was spread over too great an area of sky. This suggested it was in fact near, and if so, the failure of the 'large' 20-ft to resolve it into its component stars was disturbing. Furthermore, he was wilfully turning a blind eye to the changes that he himself, early in his career, had (he then believed) observed in its shape.

The planetary nebulae were another worry. His 1789 position was that they were star systems so compressed by attraction that they were about to experience gravitational collapse; yet the serene uniformity of their pale light argued against this. And so it was that in his private thinking, William was less dogmatic about the equation of nebulae with star clusters than his published papers suggest. Then, on 13 November 1790, he made an observation that led him to change his mind once again, and to go back to his original belief in the existence of 'true nebulosity':

> A most singular phaenomenon! A star of about the 8th magnitude, with a faint luminous atmosphere, of a circular form, and of about 3′ in diameter. The star is perfectly in the center, and the atmosphere is so diluted, faint, and equal throughout, that there can be no surmise of its consisting of stars; nor can there be a doubt of the evident connection between the atmosphere and the star.[66]

It was in fact another planetary nebula, known today as NGC 1514, but on this occasion William could see the central star, and so for him it was not a planetary but a 'nebulous star'. Observing the star, in the very centre of what looked for all the world to be a "faint luminous atmosphere", he accepted that the atmosphere

The planetary nebulae NGC 1514. William was able to see the central star with its "faint luminous atmosphere", and he concluded that the star was condensing out of the surrounding nebulosity. 'True nebulosity' therefore existed, and the question that the 40-ft had almost certainly been intended to resolve had now been answered. Photograph courtesy of Martin C. Germano.

"seems more fit to produce a star by its condensation than to depend upon the star for its existence".

Where did the luminous matter in the universe come from? It came from "the light that is perpetually emitted from millions of suns", for "the number of the emitting bodies is almost infinitely great, and the time of the continual emission indefinitely long". And so William arrives at his own version of a cyclic universe, in which light particles condense under the force of attraction into nebulae, and from these nebulae are born stars, which in turn collect into ever more condensed clusters, leading to what he was later to term "the ripening period of the globular form", clusters whose light helps the cycle to start over again.[67]

But there was loss as well as gain in his recognition of the existence of true nebulosity. In the later 1780s he had regarded the Orion Nebula and the Andromeda Nebula as star systems more than equal to our own — as galaxies greater in extent than our Galaxy. This attractive comparison now collapsed on two counts. First, unresolved nebulae such as these might be either nearby clouds of luminous fluid or distant star systems, there was no easy way to tell. Second, his gages of the Milky Way had been based on assumptions now known to be mistaken, in particular that his 20-ft could penetrate to the borders in all directions which implied that the system was of finite extent. Now he no longer knew whether our star system was finite or infinite. All he could say in 1818, in his last major paper, was that for him it was "fathomless" and possibly infinite,[68] unlike the nebulae of Orion and

"An astronomer!!", aquatint by the celebrated caricaturist Thomas Rowlandson (1756–1827), from a design by George Moutard ("Mustard") Woodward (1760–1809). This is the first of Rowlandson's *Horse Accomplishments in 12 Sketches*, published in London by Rudolph Ackermann in 1799; in each it is the horse rather than the rider that merits the title (in this case, by observing the heavens). Although there is no suggestion that this is a portrayal of William, the signpost pointing to the village of Slough ("SLOUHG") where he lived indicates that in popular imagination William was synonymous with "astronomer". Courtesy of Robert Anderson, photograph by permission of the Trustees of the National Museums of Scotland.

Andromeda which were clearly finite.

As William entered his eighth decade of life and the long nights of observing in the damp and cold took their toll, he spent less time at the telescope and more in mining his great catalogues of nebulae and clusters for the theoretical lessons to be learned from them. In 1811 and 1814 he laid out examples, first of nebulae and then of clusters, taken from his catalogues[69] and presented to the reader in what he believed to be the successive stages of development: "... there is perhaps not so much difference between [those in one category and the next] as there would be in an annual description of the human figure, were it given from the birth of a child till he comes to be a man in his prime."[70] In his last major papers,[71] written in 1817 and 1818 when he was nearly eighty, he investigated the relationship between distances and apparent magnitudes, analysing (as had Newton before him) the numbers of stars of successive magnitudes in order to test the assumption that the stars around us are distributed with reasonable uniformity, and using identical telescopes, one having diaphragms of reduced diameter, to compare the brightnesses of pairs of stars. He was innovative to the last.

William's vast collection of nebulae and clusters were re-examined by John after William's death, and re-catalogued in a format that suited the needs of observers.[72] John then journeyed to the Cape of Good Hope where he spent four years extending his father's work to the southern skies.[73] In 1864 John merged his and William's nebular discoveries with those of other observers into the *General Catalogue of Nebulae and Clusters of Stars*,[74] and in 1888 this was enlarged by J. L. E. Dreyer into the *New General Catalogue* or *NGC* that we use today.[75]

The order of distances separating us from the nearest stars had been known since Newton to be such that their light takes years to reach us. William saw the implication: "... a telescope with a power of penetrating into space ... has also, as it may be called, a power of penetrating into time past." He concluded that some of the light that reached his great reflector had been a staggering two million years on its journey, "and that consequently, so many years ago, this object must already have had an existence in the sidereal heavens, in order to send out those rays by which we now perceive it".[76] Written in 1802, half-a-century before the publication of Charles Darwin's *Origin of Species*, it was a noble insight. When William shared it with Thomas Campbell, the poet afterwards told a friend: "I really and unfeignedly felt at the moment as if I had been conversing with a supernatural intelligence."[77]

Notes and References

Abbreviations

Bennett "'On the Power of Penetrating into Space': The Telescopes of William Herschel", *Journal for the History of Astronomy*, vii (1976), 75–108.

CHA *Caroline Herschel's Autobiographies*, ed. by Michael Hoskin (Cambridge, 2003).*

Chr *The Herschel Chronicle: The Life-story of William Herschel and his Sister Caroline Herschel*, ed. by Constance A. Lubbock (Cambridge, 1933).

Construction *William Herschel and the Construction of the Heavens*, by Michael A. Hoskin (London, 1963).

Dreyer *The Scientific Papers of Sir William Herschel*, ed. by J. L. E. Dreyer (2 vols, London, 1912).

George III *The Later Correspondence of George III*, ed. by A. Aspinall, i (Cambridge, 1962).

James "Concert Life in 18th Century Bath", by Kenneth E. James (thesis, London University, 1987).

JHA *Journal for the History of Astronomy**

Mem *Memoir and Correspondence of Caroline Herschel*, by Mrs John Herschel, 2nd edn (London, 1879).

"Memorandums" "Memorandums from which an historical account of my life may be drawn", by William Herschel, Royal Astronomical Society MS Herschel W.7/8.

MH Michael Hoskin

P'ship *The Herschel Partnership: As Viewed by Caroline*, by Michael Hoskin (Cambridge, 2003).*

PT *Philosophical Transactions of the Royal Society*

RAS Royal Astronomical Society MS Herschel

SA *Stellar Astronomy: Historical Studies*, by Michael Hoskin ([Cambridge], 1982).*

Turner Science and Music in Eighteenth Century Bath, by A. J. Turner (Bath, 1977).

WH William Herschel

Citations of the form XVI, 19 (= chapter XVI, page 19) are to the original typescript of *Chr*, in the possession of The William Herschel Society, Bath.

*Available from www.shpltd.co.uk.

The Herschel Family

1 William Griesbach alone of the brothers never married and the family tree describes him as without issue, but when he died in May or June 1825 (his will was dated 13 May and proved on 25 June) he left Charles "a legacy and intrusted a Child with 2000£ to his care", Caroline to John Herschel, 15 April 1833, BL Egerton 3761. The mother of his daughter, Isabella Augusta Griesbach who was to die unmarried in 1849, may well have been the Miss Lydia White of New Windsor who is named in his will.

Preface

1 WH, "Remarks on the Construction of the Heavens", *PT*, lxxix (1789), 212–26, p. 226.

Isaac and Anna

1 *CHA*, 13.
2 For Isaac's upbringing and his early career in music, see *CHA*, 11–15.
3 *CHA*, 14.
4 *CHA*, 14–15.
5 *CHA*, 15.
6 She died in Hanover on 19 November 1789, aged 76 years and 10 months (register of the Kreuzkirche, Hanover).
7 "My dear wife ha[d] 3 brothers and 2 sisters, the eldest [brother] has died, but has left 1 son and 4 daughters. The 2nd brother has 4 daughters alive. The 3rd brother married a widow, we have not been able to find out if he has any children, he lives in the principality of Waldeck. The oldest sister is a widow. Her husband was called Röper, she has 2 sons and one daughter alive. The 2nd sister is also a widow whose husband was called Hund, they had 8 children, sons and daughters of whom two or three have died", *CHA*, 15–16.
8 *CHA*, 17.
9 *CHA*, 108.
10 On the date of the wedding and other details of the entry in the church register, see Jürgen Hamel, "Ein Beitrag zur Familiengeschichte von Friedrich Wilhelm Herschel", Gauss-Gesellschaft E. V. Göttingen, *Mitteilungen*, xxvi (1989), 99–103. This article also has detailed information on Isaac's ancestry.
11 *P'ship*, 8; *CHA*, 19–20, 98.
12 *CHA*, 20.
13 *CHA*, 98.
14 *P'ship*, 9; *CHA*, 20–21, 98–99.
15 *CHA*, 21.
16 *CHA*, 21, 99.
17 *CHA*, 21.
18 *CHA*, 21–22, 100.
19 *CHA*, 24.
20 In "Memorandums", William says that the Guards marched out of Hanover "soon after" the Lisbon earthquake of 1 November, and that "about the end of March 1756 we were at Ritzbüttel, and embarked at Cuxhawen for England, where after a passage of 16 days we

arrived in April".
21 *CHA*, 25.
22 *CHA*, 108.
23 The month is cited in the "Life-chart of Sir William Herschel" in the Herschel Family Archives.
24 *CHA*, 27, 103.
25 MH, "Was William Herschel a Deserter?", *JHA*, xxxv (2004), 356–8. William deserted, but as he was not under oath his offence was venial rather than mortal.
26 *P'ship*, 14–15.
27 *CHA*, 28.
28 *CHA*, 107.
29 *CHA*, 26.
30 *P'ship*, 17.
31 *CHA*, 31, 110. One suspects that Isaac's difficulty in obtaining a second dismission may have resulted from the blot on his army record for having connived at the desertion of his son William.
32 MH, *op. cit.* (ref. 25).
33 *CHA*, 36, 112.
34 *CHA*, 37–40, 113–15.
35 His wife Anna was to be buried beside him, and as we shall see, Caroline later bought the plot of ground so that she too could be buried there.
36 *CHA*, 40.
37 *CHA*, 19.
38 *CHA*, 110.
39 *CHA*, 24, 100. Caroline in both places portrays Isaac as assisting (rather than instructing) William in globe-making; and it was by William that she was later taught the constellations, as they journeyed through Holland on their way to England (*CHA*, 119). Isaac did show his children a solar eclipse (prudently viewed in a tub of water), but this was in 1764, long after William's departure for England (*CHA*, 112). Like many a father before and since, Isaac gave his children a taste of what astronomy had to offer, but it is a misunderstanding to imagine that he gave systematic instruction in the science to either William or Caroline.
40 *CHA*, 34.
41 *P'ship*, 23–24.

42 The Hanoverian agent in London.

43 Constance Lubbock's translation is in the Herschel Family Archives.

44 Letter of 27 February 1786, translation by Constance Lubbock in the Herschel Family Archives.

45 RAS W.1/8.

46 See ref. 6.

47 "Six years ago I had a vault built in the spot where my parents rest", *Mem*, 247.

Sophia

1 Coppenbrügge is some 50km SSW of Hanover.

2 A copy of George's memoirs is in the possession of F. Anne M. R. Jarvis, whose step-father was a descendant of Sophia; they form part of her thesis, "The Community of German Migrant Musicians in London *c.* 1750 – *c.* 1850", M.St. in Local and Regional History, University of Cambridge, 2003, which she kindly made available. The memoirs are hereafter cited as George Griesbach, Memoirs. Another descendant of Sophia, Richard Leaver, has materials relating to the Griesbach family, including details of the Griesbach entries in the church register at Coppenbrügge.

3 Caroline to Mary Herschel, 14 October 1824, BL Egerton 3761.

4 The speculation to this effect in *P'ship*, 9, has since been confirmed by George Griesbach, Memoirs.

5 Family records give the date of his birth.

6 The date is given in the register of the Coppenbrügge parish register. He was buried on 3 February.

7 *CHA*, 23.

8 *CHA*, 23.

9 Caroline to Mary Herschel, 14 October 1824, BL Egerton 3761.

10 The following is based upon "Genealogy of the Griesbach family" in the possession of Richard Leaver.

11 His third son from his first marriage, Konrad Ludwig (1728–59), was again a surgeon, as was his only son from the second marriage, Johann Heinrich Christoff (1741–?), though the church records make it clear that he was no more than a barber-surgeon.

12 The date is given in "Genealogy of the Griesbach family".

13 *CHA*, 22.

14 *CHA*, 24, 102.

15 *CHA*, 25.

16 The month is cited in the "Life-chart of Sir William Herschel" in the Herschel Family Archives.

17 This date is sometimes given as the 10th, but the memoirs written by George himself in the 1810s state that he was born on the 11th, as does *CHA*, 28, and "Genealogy of the Griesbach family".

18 *CHA*, 28, 106.

19 *CHA*, 107.

20 It seems unlikely that Heinrich would have quit the army until he was confident of being able to support his family by other means, and he would hardly have envisaged a prolonged residence in French-occupied Hanover, so the probability is that he secured the Coppenbrügge post before requesting dismission.

21 Papers in the possession of Anne Jarvis detail Heinrich's position and duties in Coppenbrügge.

22 Caroline to Mary Herschel, 14 October 1824, BL Egerton 3761.

23 George Griesbach, Memoirs.

24 The dates of their births (and, in one case, death) and the death of Heinrich are recorded in the Coppenbrügge parish register.

25 "Genealogy of the Griesbach family".

26 *CHA*, 40.

27 On 18 December 1822, BL Egerton 3761, Caroline mentions to Mary Herschel a letter that her brother Dietrich has received from Friderica and which he is forwarding to William Griesbach. In 1825 William Griesbach left her £500 (Caroline to Mary Baldwin, 3 June 1825, *ibid*.); she is "here in Germany (but I thank God far

from Han[over])".

28 According to the note on the silhouette in the Herschel Family Archives.

29 Caroline to Mary Herschel (ref. 22).

30 "Griesbach had contracted depts, which with Alexander's salary from his place in the [Court] Orchestra (who was with 2 years leave at Bath working hard) and with the assistance of your dear Husband they were liquidated", Caroline to Mary Herschel (ref. 22).

31 George Griesbach, Memoirs.

32 *Ibid.*

33 *Ibid.*

34 This is confirmed by George who speaks of "my place at Coppenbrügge", *ibid.*

35 *Ibid.*

36 *Ibid.*

37 "Of Charles, my next brother, I could not think, as he was in my place at Coppenbrügge", *ibid.*

38 The entry in vol. vi of *A Biographical Dictionary of Actors, Actresses, Musicians, Dancers, Managers and Other Stage Personnel in London, 1660–1800*, by Philip. H. Highfield, Jr, Kalman A. Burnim and Edward A. Langhams (Carbondale and Edwardsville, 1978), states that he came to England in 1780 at the request of the King. From what George tells us, Henry must have arrived in England either in late 1779, or in 1780.

39 According to a letter (English translation by Constance Lubbock in the Herschel Family Archives) written by Jacob to William in May 1783, Sophia moved back to Hanover that summer. Anna died in November 1789 and Jacob was murdered

in 1792, but Dietrich would be resident in the town with his wife and children for the rest of Sophia's life.

40 Letter from Jacob to William Herschel, May 1785, English translation by Constance Lubbock in the Herschel Family Archives. George Griesbach visited his mother in Hanover that summer, arriving on 3 July (Memoirs).

41 William to Caroline, 14 July 1786, RAS W.1/8.12.

42 The date of 1788 comes from Griesbach family records. In his memoirs, George says that he visited Hanover for health reasons when he "had been in England near ten years" (that is, before May 1788) and that "it was soon after this that I got William over". Anne Jarvis (*op. cit.* (ref. 2)) points out that Charles Burney, in his *An Account of the Musical Performances in Westminster Abbey, and the Pantheon … in Commemoration of Handel* (London, 1785), 17–19, cites the participation of three Griesbachs including "Griesbach Jnr.", and this may indicate that Frederick was in London in 1784.

43 George Griesbach, Memoirs.

44 The date is interpolated in a later hand in George's memoirs. *Chr*, 316, is in error in saying that Charles joined the band only after his mother's death in 1803; on p. 295 the author had quoted Charles Burney as saying that already in July 1799 William's five nephews were "a principal part of the band".

45 The register of the Garrisonsgemeinde, Hanover, states that "Soph. Doroth. Griesebach" [*sic*] died on 30 March and was buried on 3 April.

Jacob

1 *CHA*, 20.

2 *CHA*, 20.

3 Reading, writing and (for the boys) arithmetic, *P'ship*, 7.

4 *CHA*, 100.

5 "End of Decr 1747, 'Jacob engaged in the Garde'", *CHA*, 99, citing a memorandum of Isaac.

6 *CHA*, 99.

7 On 1 May ("Memorandums").

8 *CHA*, 22.

9 *CHA*, 21.

10 *CHA*, 100.

11 *CHA*, 25, 101; *P'ship*, 12–13.

12 *CHA*, 101.

13 *CHA*, 102.

14 *CHA*, 27.

15 *CHA*, 28.

16 *CHA*, 28, 106.

17 *CHA*, 106.

18 "Memorandums".

19 II, 2. As Caroline wrote to William's son John after William's death, "So it happened, my dear nephew, that your father was his brother's fag; by teaching, writing music for what he could get, to keep him [Jacob] from the degradation of accepting any engagement under a leader or first violin", *Chr*, 12.

20 RAS W.7/8, 10.

21 "Memorandums".

22 II, 2.

23 IV, 2.

24 *CHA*, 30.

25 *CHA*, 31.

26 *CHA*, 111.

27 *CHA*, 31.

28 *CHA*, 39.

29 "Memorandums".

30 They survive in the Herschel Family Archives.

31 *CHA*, 41, 115.

32 *P'ship*, 22.

33 "Memorandums", and MH, "Vocations in Conflict: William Herschel in Bath, 1766–1782", *History of Science*, xli (2003), 315–33, p. 318.

34 *CHA*, 43.

35 *P'ship*, 22, 116.

36 *CHA*, 44.

37 *CHA*, 45.

38 *CHA*, 45.

39 *CHA*, 46.

40 *CHA*, 116.

41 *CHA*, 47.

42 *CHA*, 47.

43 *CHA*, 48; *P'ship*, 23–24.

44 *CHA*, 48.

45 From the translation by Constance Lubbock, in the Herschel Family Archives.

46 *Berlinsche Musikalische Zeitung* for 1793, 133–4, cited in ref. 50 below.

47 RAS W.1/8.

48 *Mem*, 75; *CHA*, 93.

49 Translation by Constance Lubbock, in the Herschel Family Archives.

50 "Um noch einmal auf Jacob Herschel zuruechzukommen: er endete auf tragische Weise. Man fand ihn am 23. Juni 1792 erwuergt auf dem Felde in der List, vor den Toren Hannovers. Ueber die naeheren Umstaende seines Todes war Bestimmtes nicht mehr zu erfahren" ("To return once more to the death of Jacob Herschel: he ended in a tragic way. He was found on 23 June 1792 strangled in a field in The List, outside the gates of Hanover. No further details of the incident could be determined"), Heinrich Sievers, *Hannoversche Musikgeschichte* (Tutzing, 1979), 365. This is confirmed by the short-lived *Berlinsche Musikalische Zeitung* for 1793. An editorial item on pp. 133–4 concerning music in Hanover, based on a letter received from there, states: "Der Vice-Konzertmeister, Jacob Herschel, ward im vorigen Jahre im Felde erwürgt gefunden, und schon lange ist keine Stelle wieder besetzt worden ..." ("The Vice-Concertmaster Jacob Herschel was found last year strangled in a field, and the position has since been vacant ..."). It could well be that the archives of the Court Orchestra would shed further light, but there is no trace of these either in Hanover or in the British Royal Archives.

Johann Heinrich

1 CHA, 19.

2 CHA, 20.

William

1 *CHA*, 15–16.

2 "Memorandums", 6.

3 "Memorandums", 6.

4 *CHA*, 21.

5 "Memorandums", 7.

6 "Memorandums", 7.

7 "Memorandums", 7.

8 "Memorandums", 7.

9 "Memorandums", 8.

10 "Memorandums", 8.

11 The month is cited in a life-chart of William in the Herschel Family Archives.

12 CHA, 103.

13 "Memorandums", 8.

14 J. B. Sidgwick, *William Herschel* (London, 1953), 21.

15 "Memorandums", 9.

16 "Memorandums", 9.

17 CHA, 103; *P'ship*, 5.

18 "Memorandums", 9.

19 "Memorandums", 9.

20 "Memorandums", 9.

21 CHA, 106.

22 "Memorandums", 9.

23 "Memorandums", 9–10.

24 CHA, 106.

25 II, 1.

26 *Ibid.*

27 *Ibid.*

28 "So it happened, my dear nephew, that your father was his brother's fag; by teaching, writing music for what he could get, to keep him [Jacob] from the degradation of accepting any engagement under a leader or first violin", Caroline to John, *Chr*, 12. She enlarges on this in "Biographical Memorandums of my Nephew", BL M/588(4): "... by writing music, teaching for what he could get &c &c and was at last left alone to pay tailors bills & and parting with the last farthing for traveling expenses."

29 "Memorandums", 10.

30 CHA, 106.

31 See Owen Gingerich, "William Herschel's 1784 Biography", *Harvard Library Bulletin*, xxxii/1 (Winter 1984), 73–82.

32 11 June 1761, III, 17.

33 III, 25–26.

34 It is printed in full in Dreyer, i, p. xvi.

35 "Memorandums", 10–11.

36 II, 3.

37 "... by making the journey to Durham on foot and other privations he was extricated at once out of his difficulties", *ibid.*

38 Letter to Jacob, 22 January 1762, III, 24.

39 When the day came that he found himself an itinerant musician wholly dependent on fees, he told Jacob that "... I am almost tired of having no home or place to be fixed in", 13 March 1762, III, 25.

40 William had already composed a D minor viola concerto by August 1759, that is, while he and Jacob were still together in southeast England, and he composed another, in F major, in London a few weeks later. An extended analysis of the F major is to be found in Robert F. Royce, "An Early Musical Work of William Herschel: The Concerto in F major for Viola, Strings and Continuo", *The Speculum: The Journal of the William Herschel Society*, iv/2 (Winter 2005/06), 37–44. In the same journal, v/1 (Summer 2006), 2–8, Royce contributes "An Overview of Herschel's Musical Production". For a list of William's compositions, see Annexe VI (pp. 243–58) of Ronald Lessens, *William Herschel: Musicien et Astronome* (Vannes, 2004), and Frank Brown, *William Herschel: Musician & Composer* (The William Herschel Society, Bath, 1990). Lessens reproduces the opening bars of many of William's compositions.

41 Gingerich, *op. cit.* (ref. 31), 79.

42 With far-reaching implications, as we shall shortly see.

43 "Memorandums", 12–13.

44 When William visited Hanover in 1764, he retrieved his letters from Jacob, and they are now in the Herschel Family Archives.

45 "Memorandums", 13–14.

46 Letter of 11 March 1761, II, 14.

47 II, 11.

48 Letter of 11 March 1761, II, 13.

49 Letter of 10 July 1761, II, 19.

50 Edward Augustus (1739–67), Duke of York and Albany.

51 II, 19.

52 Letter of 16 November 1761, II, 23.

53 Letter of 22 January 1762, III, 24.

54 Letter of 13 March 1762, III, 25.

55 Letter of 25 April 1762, III, 26.

56 *Ibid.*

57 Letter of 25 April 1762, III, 27.

58 *P'ship*, 21.

59 III, 30.

60 Letter of 2 April 1763, III, 32.

61 "Memorandums", 20.

62 "Memorandums": "1766 Nov 30. For the 13 Sundays of my being organist I was paid 13 Guineas."

63 "Memorandums": "1766 July ... Organ every day by way of practice at Leeds."

64 "Memorandums": "1766 Aug 9. Letter from Mrs De Chair...."

65 The chapel was built 1766–67 from a subscription organized by Rev. Dr John de Chair (1729–1810) and William Street, a banker, and remained in use until 1895 (Turner, 31). For details of the layout of the chapel, see *ibid*. How William came to be known in Bath is unclear. Turner, 25, documents contemporary musical links between Yorkshire and the West of England; for example, from 1772 members of the Ladies Chorus of the North of England assisted the trebles at Gloucester in the Three Choirs Festival. It is also curious that it was Mrs De Chair who conducted the correspondence, rather than her husband. Presumably she had met William on some occasion. Lubbock, *Chr*, 37, speculates that she might have been a pupil of William's, although this is unlikely as he had never been in the West of England. An excellent account of the building of the Octagon Chapel and its role in the religious and musical life of Bath is by Trevor Fawcett, "William Herschel at the Octagon Chapel, Bath", *The Speculum: The Journal of the William Herschel Society*, v/2 (2006/7), 7–13. At the time of writing, the Octagon, which is on the east side of Milson Street, is undergoing restoration for secular use.

66 "Memorandums": "1766 Aug 29. Letter from Mrs Dechair in which I was nominated as the intended Organist of an organ to be erected in the Octagon chapel at Bath."

67 "Memorandums": "1766 Aug 30. Another Canditate for the Organist's place played first after which I also played. The Messieurs Bates and principal Gentlemen of the Town were in the body of the church, and it was unanimously decided that I was to be their Organist." The

famous story in chap. 66 of Robert Southey's *The Doctor* (London, 1834–47) whereby William produced a slow, solemn harmony by placing lead weights on two of the keys is conveniently available in *Chr*, 37.

68 "Memorandums": "1766 Sept. 2. Letter to Mrs Dechair."

69 James, 698. This thesis — unfortunately not published — is a major source for our knowledge of William's musical activities in Bath.

70 "Memorandums", entry for 1766 Oct 22.

71 J. Haslewood, *The Secret History of the Green Room, containing authentic and entertaining memoirs of the actors and actresses of the three Theatres Royal*, 3rd edn (London, 1793), ii, Appendix, p. xv. This little episode in William's life was elucidated by James, 469–71. Elizabeth Harper may be the "Miss Hooper" who sang in William's very first concert in Bath on New Year's Day, 1767 (S. Derrick, *Letters written by Samuel Derrick* (London, 1767), ii, 102).

72 "Memorandums": "1767 Jan 1. A Benefit Concert at Rooms, the Music chiefly of my composition. I had but little company but it was select. I performed a solo concert on the violin, one on the Hautboy and a Sonata on the Harpsichord."

73 "Memorandums": 1767 Jan 23.

74 Turner, 34.

75 Edward Rack, cited by Turner, 39.

76 "Memorandums": "1767 Jan 23. Letter from Mr Derrick, the master of the Ceremonies, offering me a Situation in the established Band of Musicians that played at the public Subscription concerts, the Pumproom, the Balls, the Play House, &c &c. This I at first refused but some time after accepted when I found that Mr Lindley the first Musician in the place was one of this band and that like him I might be allowed to send a deputy when not convenient to attend personally." On the Linleys, see James, *passim*, and Turner, 35–37.

77 *Bath Chronicle*, 8 January 1767, cited by James, 699.

78 James, 699. As we shall see, when the actor John Bernard took lessons from

William, there was a cello in the room; and the oboe was the instrument that William had played as a teenager in the band of the Hanoverian Guards. On the other hand, Brown, *op. cit.* (ref. 40), 10, maintains: "It is unlikely that he taught the oboe, for in an age of rigid social conventions it was not considered a suitable instrument for ladies and gentlemen."

79 "Memorandums": 1767 March 28, April 16. On 15 July William moved to a different house in Beauford Square, and on 1 June 1769 to 7 New King Street.

80 Turner, 31–33, gives full details of the organ and its maker.

81 "Dr Dechair intending to introduce Cathedral Service, I had prepared a Choir of Singers and composed the required Music for the purpose, which on account of its simplicity was generally approved of", note added on p. 27 of "Memorandums". Ozias Linley, son of Thomas and a pupil of William, spoke of "their intrinsic merit as devotional compositions", and one of William's psalm settings was published in Bath as late as 1825, Turner, 33. William's list of vocal compositions in his possession (RAS W.7/11) includes "Three Morning and Evening Services, and the 51st Psalm" in addition to anthems for Christmas and Easter. But the bulk of the works he wrote for the choir were left behind at Bath in a box.

82 "Memorandums": "1767 June 29. The organ began to be put up."

83 "Memorandums": "1767 July 25. Letters to Mssrs Norris, Price and Mathews to engage them for the oratorios to be performed at the opening of the Octagon Chapel." The chapel was opened on 4 October, *ibid.* In the spring of 1766, William had been leader of the orchestra in a performance of *Messiah* to inaugurate the new organ at Halifax parish church, "Memorandums", 20.

84 From *Neues Hannöverisches Magazin* for 1804, cited in *Chr*, 41.

85 "Memorandums": "1767 Octr 28. Oratorio in the morning; Concert at Rooms in the evening."

86 "Memorandums": "1773 Nov 15. Attended 46

private Scholars; nearly 8 per day."

87 The actor John Bernard, however, tells us that William refused any payment from him. John Bernard, *Retrospections of the Stage*, ed. by W. B. Bernard (London, 1830), ii, 63.

88 "Memorandums", 31.

89 "Memorandums", 31.

90 *Bath Chronicle*, 13 June 1768. In his "Memorandums" for this month, William notes: "Spring Garden Concerts twice a week." He mentions in his list of manuscripts of compositions for voice, "Madrigals, Catches and Glees in parts; with the Scores of some of them. They were all performed at the Spring-Garden Concerts at Bath" (RAS W.7/11, 18).

91 In his own list of "Instrumental Musical Compositions" (RAS W.7/11, 17), William includes "Two printed copies of six Harpsichord Lessons for Scholars". That these — the only substantial publication of music composed by William — were students' exercises was unknown to Brown (*op. cit.* (ref. 40)), who discusses them as though they were intended for public performance.

92 His list of "Vocal Musical compositions" (RAS W.7/11, 18–19) lists the arias, duets and choruses of "The Success of Satan Against Man", and the handful of completed items for "The Desert Island". In 1769 William earned £316 ("Memorandums", 28) and two years later this had risen to nearly £400 (29). The Astronomer Royal's salary was £300.

93 Ian Woodfield, *The Celebrated Quarrel between Thomas Linley (senior) and William Herschel: An episode in the musical life of 18th century Bath* (typescript pamphlet, University of Bath, 1977).

94 James, 704.

95 *P'ship*, 23–24; *CHA*, 48, 117.

96 *P'ship*, 25; *CHA*, 118.

97 "Memorandums", 20.

98 William Emerson (1701–82), author of *The Doctrine of Fluxions* (London, 1743). See the entry in *Dictionary of National Biography*.

99 Colin Maclaurin (1698–1746), whose works included *A Treatise on Fluxions* (Edinburgh, 1742), see the entry in *Dictionary of*

Scientific Biography.

100 James Hodgson (1672–1755), author of *The Doctrine of Fluxions Founded upon Sir Isaac Newton's Method* (London, 1736), see the entry in *Dictionary of National Biography.*

101 Robert Smith (1689–1768), Plumian professor of astronomy at Cambridge, and a decisive influence on William. As a musician, William had understandably wished to read Smith's *Harmonics, or The Philosophy of Musical Sounds* (Cambridge, 1749), and his satisfaction with this work was later to lead him to the same author's *A Compleat System of Opticks* (Cambridge, 1738). This work was to inspire William's early work in the construction of telescopes, and also helped direct his astronomical thinking. See the entry on Smith in *Dictionary of Scientific Biography.*

102 Gingerich, *op. cit.* (ref. 31), 79.

103 There is no firm evidence as to when William bought Smith's *Opticks*, but we have seen that among the books he lists as reading matter during his last months in Yorkshire are "Dr Smith's Harmonics &c". William assembled his memoranda very late in life (Caroline in letter to John, 25 September 1827, says "I suppose it was in the year of 1818 or perhaps earlier", BL Egerton 3761), but his failure to mention at this point such a significant purchase as *Opticks* would prove to be, suggests that he bought this work after he was settled in Bath. That he was so keen to visit opticians' shops while passing through London with Caroline in August 1772 makes it likely that he had bought *Opticks* in the previous year or two.

104 "Memorandums", 20.

105 Gingerich, *op. cit.* (ref. 31), 79; RAS W.5/12.1, 5.

106 *P'ship*, 28–32; *CHA*, 49–52, 119–22.

107 In RAS W.5/12.1,1, he states that it was a Hadley's quadrant. He used it in particular to measure the altitude of the Sun both before noon and after. Noon itself was midway between two such times when the altitudes were equal, and this allowed William to determine the error in his clock.

108 William Emerson, *Elements of Trigonometry* (London, 1749).

109 At the beginning of RAS W.5/12.1, he states the book to have been James Ferguson's *Astronomy Explained upon Sir Isaac Newton's Principles*, of which the first edition had appeared in London in 1756.

110 "Memorandums", 31.

111 Smith, *Opticks*, ii, 447.

112 Smith, *Opticks*, ii, 447–8. Bradley had failed to detect annual parallax in a number of stars, and the known accuracy of the instrument he was using therefore put an upper limit on their parallax and so a lower limit on their distances.

113 Smith, *Opticks*, ii, 447–8.

114 And the subject of an entry in *Dictionary of Scientific Biography.*

115 Ferguson, *Astronomy* (ref. 109), para. 13, 10.

116 Ismael Bulliardus, *Ad Astronomos Monita Duo* (Paris, 1667), Monitum Alterum.

117 Gingerich, *op. cit.* (ref. 31), 79.

118 *P'ship*, 34; *CHA*, 52. The date of 22 September is given in "Memorandums". Caroline's chronology seems to imply that the purchase was made earlier in the year, but she is writing long after the event.

119 *CHA*, 52.

120 In November 1778, for example, he directed a Musical Meeting at Trowbridge with "most approved performers" from Bath, though the seats were only half the five shillings normal in Bath (*Bath Chronicle*, 8 November 1778).

121 *P'ship*, 37; *CHA*, 54, 127.

122 Christiaan Huygens, *Systema Saturnium* (The Hague, 1659), 8. The image is available on-line at www.sil.si.edu/digitalcollections/HST/Huygens/huygens-ill8.htm.

123 *CHA*, 55.

124 Caroline says that the house was near Walcot Turnpike, and this has been accepted as correct. However, Professor Thomas Hornsby of Oxford in December 1774 addressed a letter to William "near Walcot Parade" (RAS W.1/13.H.23), and William himself later wrote from Hanover to Caroline at "Walcot Parade" (letter of 22 August 1777, in the Herschel Family Archives). On the other hand, RAS W.7/1

lists "Observations by the Regulator on the Wall ... at Walcot turn pike house". The Parade was much closer to the centre of the town than was the turnpike.

125 *CHA*, 55.

126 RAS W.3/1.4, 1–4, p. 2.

127 *Ibid.*, p. 8.

128 *Ibid.*, p. 10.

129 Bennett, 76–81.

130 Turner, 33.

131 James, 210–13, 705.

132 James, 214, 705.

133 Bernard, *Retrospections* (ref. 87), ii, 58, cited in part by James, 700.

134 *Ibid.*, 60–61.

135 "Memorandums", 34, entry for 1782 Jan/Feb.

136 Bernard, *Retrospections* (ref. 87), 59.

137 *Ibid.*, 60. The Green Room is the actors' changing room in a theatre.

138 *Ibid.*, 62–63.

139 James, 214–15.

140 "Memorandums", 32.

141 James, 218. Despite his summer devotion to astronomy, William — perhaps surprisingly, in the light of the picture Caroline presents — was not averse to the occasional profitable musical engagement. Public breakfasts with music and dancing were a traditional means of charitable fundraising, for tradesmen fallen on hard times, widows, children born blind, and so forth, but the *Bath Chronicle* records that in June 1778 the music was directed by William and took the form of a full-blown concert. On 28 May the *Chronicle* had also advertised "Evening Amusements" at Spring Gardens with vocal and instrumental music with illuminations, after the manner of Vauxhall in London. The first concert was given on 18 June, and according to the *Chronicle* some seven hundred attended. William was almost certainly involved, for in his "Memorandums" for the following year he notes the music he composed for these occasions: "In Summer we had Concerts in Spring Gardens for which I composed Glees, Madrigals, Songs and Duettos. Among them was the Echo Catch, which had

a great run" ("Memorandums", May 1779, confirmed by his list of surviving compositions, RAS W.7/11).

142 *P'ship*, 42.

143 "Memorandums", 1779 May.

144 MH, "Newton, Providence and the Universe of Stars", *JHA*, viii (1977), 77–101, p. 82.

145 MH, "Stellar Distances: Galileo's Method and its Subsequent History", *Indian Journal of History of Science*, i (1966), 22–29. The method did not originate with Galileo but with his little-known correspondent Lodovico Ramponi, see Harald Siebert, "The Early Search for Stellar Parallax: Galileo, Castelli, and Ramponi", *JHA*, xxxvi (2005), 251–71.

146 RAS W.2/1.1, 49–53.

147 John Michell, "An Enquiry into the Probable Parallax and Magnitude of the Fixed Stars", *PT*, lvii (1767), 234–64.

148 RAS W.2/1.1, 5.

149 It was to be followed by a more extensive review with higher magnification, a work that William completed on 26 September 1783, just before he embarked on his programme of sweeps for nebulae.

150 On William's telescopes, see Bennett.

151 *P'ship*, 42–44.

152 Reprinted in Dreyer.

153 See Angus Armitage, *William Herschel* (London, 1962), chap. 3, and A. F. O'D. Alexander, *The Planet Uranus: A History of Observation, Theory and Discovery* (London, 1965), chap. 1.

154 "Memorandums", 34.

155 *Chr*, 79–81.

156 WH, "Catalogue of Double Stars", *PT*, lxxii (1782), 112–62.

157 WH, "Astronomical Observations Relating to the Mountains on the Moon", *PT*, lxx (1780), 507–26.

158 Letter of 18 December 1781, RAS W.1/13. W.12.

159 Letter of 25 December 1781, RAS W.1/13. W.13.

160 *Ibid.*

161 Letter of 22 January 1782, RAS W.1/13.A.8.

162 The saga of William's over-ambitious attempt is detailed in RAS W.5/12.1, 48–58.

163 In his "Description of a Forty-feet Reflecting Telescope" (*PT*, lxxxv (1795), 347–409, p.

348), William says categorically that he "invented and executed a stand for it". In his notebook (RAS W.5/12.1, 56) he speaks of the stand itself in the present tense, but says "The tube is intended ...". In a letter to John dated 7 March 1825, Caroline mentions that "timber for the erection of the 30-ft telescope of which the casting of the mirror was pretty far advanced was thought of" (BL Egerton 3761).

164 Bennett, 81.

165 Letter of 31 August 1781, RAS W.1/13.W.9.

166 RAS W.5/12.1, 58.

167 *CHA*, 64.

168 James, 235.

169 *P'ship*, 51; *CHA*, 64–65.

170 *Bonner and Middleton's Bristol Journal*, 30 March 1782, cited by James, 236.

171 James, 237.

172 On Demainbray, see Alan Q. Norton and Jane A. Wess, *Public & Private Science: The King George III Collection* (Oxford, 1993), chap. IV: "The Career of S. C. T. Demainbray (1710–82)". Demainbray was paid £210 on 14 May 1755 for a "Course of Natural & Experimental Philosophy for their Royal Highnesses" the Prince of Wales and Prince Edward (p. 106). The same year he was granted a pension of £100 from King George II, but had difficulty in securing payment, and so he was forced to return to giving courses of public lectures in London (pp. 106, 111). He petitioned, apparently without success, to be librarian to the Prince of Wales (pp. 106, 109).

An older account, based on family papers, is Gibbes Rigaud, "Dr. Demainbray and the King's Observatory at Kew", *The Observatory*, v (1882), 279–85. According to this account, "When His Majesty George III came to the age of eighteen [1756], and governors and teachers were dismissed, Dr. Demainbray was pleased to have the sole trust of teaching him sciences till he came to the throne; Queen Charlotte, after her marriage with the King, also became his pupil and listened to his lectures in philosophy..." (p. 281).

173 The archives of Kew Observatory are held at King's College London. The transit observations are in K/MUS 1/1.

174 K/MUS 1/7 contains daily temperature, barometric and rainfall readings taken at Kew between 1773 and 1783.

175 Rigaud, *op. cit.* (ref. 172), 282.

176 *Chr*, 112.

177 *Chr*, 113. There is little doubt that what Lubbock says is correct, although she cites no source, but just when the King made his promise publicly known is unclear. Certainly Watson continued to cherish hopes of Kew for many weeks to come, as we shall see.

178 RAS W.1/13.D.14, letter of Demainbray to William, 12 August 1781. Cf. *P'ship*, 50.

179 Letter in the British Museum — Natural History, Dawson Turner Collection, ii, 108, cited by Norton and Wess, *op. cit.* (ref. 172), 35.

180 "Memorandums", 34.

181 British Museum — Natural History, Dawson Turner Collection, ii, 118–19, cited by Norton and Wess, *op. cit.* (ref. 172), 35.

182 Walsh to William, 10 May 1782, RAS W.1/13. W.5.

183 *CHA*, 65.

184 Caroline gives his day of departure as the Tuesday, *CHA*, 65.

185 *CHA*, 65: "A new 7 ft Stand and Steps were made to go in a moderate sized box for to be screwed together on the spot where wanted."

186 Namely γ Vir, γ Leo, π Boo, 54 Leo, Castor, γ Her, α Cyg, γ And and γ Vir, RAS W.2/1.4, f. 12. Rightly or wrongly, William assumed the King would be a serious observer and interested to see examples of William's more challenging discoveries.

187 *Chr*, 115.

188 *P'ship*, 46.

189 Aubert to William, 19 October 1786, RAS W.1/13.A.26.

190 *Chr*, 114.

191 Watson still entertained hopes as late as 29 June, when he wrote to Banks: "... nothing remains now to be done in order to gain him the Post he so much covets, than to inform the King of these particulars, & of Mr Herschel's ardent wishes to serve his Majesty by succeeding the late Dr

Demainbray" (British Museum — Natural History, Dawson Turner Collection, ii, 144, cited by Norton and Wess, *op. cit.* (ref. 172), 35).

192 William to Caroline, 25 May 1782, RAS W.1/8.

193 RAS W.4/1.3.

194 *Chr*, 115.

195 Lindley, known to William as Linley, was Maskelyne's assistant from 1781 to 1786, Eric G. Forbes, *Greenwich Observatory*, i: *Origins and Early History (1675–1835)* (London, 1975), 150.

196 RAS W.4/1.3.

197 *Chr*, 115.

198 *Ibid.*, 116.

199 RAS W.4/1.3.

200 William to Alexander, 10 June 1782, RAS W.1/9.

201 *Ibid.*

202 RAS W.4/1.3.

203 Watson to William, 12 June 1782, RAS W.1/13.W.16.

204 Watson to William, 23 June 1782, RAS W.1/13.W.17.

205 Hornsby to William, 22 December 1774, RAS W.1/13/H.23.

206 RAS W.1/13.W.18.

207 In a letter to Margaret Herschel, 3 February 1842, BL Egerton 3762.

208 In time all five of the brothers were to be members of the band.

209 RAS W.4/1.3.

210 *Chr*, 118.

211 *Chr*, 119.

212 "A Letter from William Herschel", *PT*, lxxiii (1783), 1–3.

213 Watson to William, 14 July 1782, RAS W.1/13. W.19.

214 *CHA*, 66.

215 RAS W.4/1.3.

216 *P'ship*, 57–58.

217 *P'ship*, 57.

218 RAS W.4/1.3.

219 *Chr*, 134.

220 XI, 24. For a detailed account of the property, see *P'ship*, 57–59.

221 RAS W.2/1.4, 25v.

222 *Ibid.*, 26r.

223 *Ibid.*, 39r. This may again be M 11, which

according to Halley (and Ferguson) preceded the right foot of Antinous.

224 RAS W.4/1.3.

225 *CHA*, 69. William's visit to Bath must have been within the period 8–17 December, for this is the only gap of sufficient length in his observing record.

226 MH, "Unfinished Business: William Herschel's Sweeps for Nebulae", *History of Science*, xviii (2005), 305–20. William first used the 20-ft for sweeping on 28 October 1783, and completed 45 solo sweeps before beginning his long partnership with Caroline on 18 December. See Royal Society MSS 339 and 272.

227 His records of "Experiments on the Construction of Specula" (RAS W.5/12.1) for April 1779 mention his polishing specula for Alexander (experiment 1/202), Caroline (1/210) and Dietrich (1/217). In his letter of June 1782 (RAS W.1/13.W.16), Watson mentions viewing the Moon. Other acquaintances were also favoured: in William's experiment 1/251 he speaks of preparing a 7-ft speculum for a Mr Parsons, and in 1/252 a 3-ft Gregorian mirror for John B. Bryant of Bath.

228 *Chr*, 133.

229 RAS W.7/8, 35–36.

230 MH, "George III's Purchase of Herschel Reflectors", *JHA*, in press.

231 John Tracy Spaight, "'For the Good of Astronomy': The Manufacture, Sale and Distant Use of William Herschel's Telescopes", *JHA*, xxxv (2004), 45–69.

232 On 9 March 1794 William wrote to Walter Shairp in St Petersburg with a price list, the larger sizes being offered either with or without the stand (which could be made by a local carpenter). A small 7-ft cost 100 guineas (£105), a large 20-ft cost 2000 guineas with stand or 1000 guineas without, while a 40-ft with 4-ft mirror cost either 8000 or 4000 guineas. See RAS W.1/1.

233 Topman Beauclerk, great-grandson of Charles II and Nell Gwynne, had sold the property to Sir Edward Walpole, whose illegitimate daughter Laura married Frederic Keppel, Bishop of Exeter. Laura inherited the property in 1784 (Herschel

Family Archives).

234 *Chr*, 174.

235 *Chr*, 174.

236 William Watson, Jr, to William, 24 March 1788, RAS W.1/13.W.51.

237 Elizabeth Baldwin died on 22 October 1798, and left the Herschel home (and Elizabeth's own garden adjacent to it) to Mary, and the rest of her property equally to Mary and her brother John, National Archives, PROB 11/1314.

238 XI, 20–21. Matters did not in fact proceed as quickly as Watson would have wished. As early as 25 August 1784 (RAS W.1/13. W.32), he was asking William "Has the King set you about the magnum opus, the great speculum?", but it was to be nearly a year before William made the formal application. Only on 24 September 1785 was Watson able to send William his congratulations on the grant that would enable him "to undertake that glorious telescope which will excel all other instruments of that sort to so great a degree" (13.W.39).

239 RAS W.5/12.1, 69.

240 *Chr*, 144.

241 See ref. 232 above.

242 Caroline to John, 27 October 1830, BL Egerton 3761. William became a knight of the Hanoverian Guelphic Order in 1816.

243 Watson to William, 11 November 1785, RAS W.1/13.W.40.

244 *Chr*, 147.

245 *George III*, Letter 379.

246 XI 19b; letter of Caroline to Margaret Herschel, wife of John, 10 January 1840, BL Egerton 3762.

247 RAS W.1/5.2(i).

248 The twenty-three receipts for equipment and salary lodged by William and his sister between February 1786 (soon after construction commenced) and July 1790 (when William considered the instrument to be in operation) amount to only £2947 10s. 0d. (*George III*, 456, fn), which suggests that William's second application was for an appropriate sum and that the additional £1000 was not in fact required.

249 RAS W.1/13.B.20.

250 *Mem*, 209.

251 RAS W.1/13.W.50.

252 *Mem*, 211.

253 See Roy Porter, *Mind Forg'd Manacles: Madness and Psychiatry in England from Restoration to Regency* (London, 1987).

254 Personal communication, 13 November 1997.

255 *George III*, Letter 656.

256 In 1786 William had become an LL.D. *honoris causa* of Edinburgh University.

257 *George III*, Letter 570.

258 The first repolishing of the successful mirror began in July 1790 (RAS W.5/12.1, p. 128), so this letter presumably dates from July or August of that year.

259 *George III*, Letter 432.

260 So for example Cassini de Thury writes to William on 15 February 1785 to say that he plans to visit England next year to see William's telescopes "et de faire connaissance avec vous en sera le principal objet" of his visit, RAS W.1/13. C.6. Lalande writes on 8 November 1786: "J'espere l'été prochain aller lui rendre mes hommages, et voir votre superbe telescope de 40 piedes", L.4; on 26 April 1787 he writes: "M. Sniadecki, professeur d'astronomie à Cracovie, ne pouvant retourner dans sa patrie sans aller visiter le premier sanctuaire de cette science ...", L.5; on 12 May 1787 he asks if the 40-ft is now operational, and if so he will come to England to see it, L.6; and on 21 May 1788 he again hopes for news of its completion: "Je prie M. Darquier de me donner des nouvelles du telescope de quarante pieds que j'attends pour faire le voyage d'Angleterre", L.8.

261 RAS W.2/2.8, ff. 2v–3r.

262 Caroline later lamented the time wasted on this mirror, to the extent of making the unlikely assertion that their brother Alexander "would more than once have destroyed it secretly if I had not persuaded him against it", letter to John, April 1827, BL Egerton 3761.

263 Letter to Charles Blagden, 27 November 1786, RAS W.1/1, 151–3.

264 RAS W.5/12.1, 114.

265 26 December 1793; it lasted just half an hour before being replaced by manpower, RAS

W.5/12.3, expt 3.

266 RAS W.2/1.1, 1.

267 William made his first sketch of the configuration of the satellites on 18 April 1783 (RAS W.3/1.8), and did this again several times in the weeks that followed. He observed the satellites four times in the summer of 1784 and once in 1785, after which he neglected them until August 1787.

268 Letter of 8 November 1786, RAS W.1/13. L.4.

269 RAS W.3/1.8. For a careful account of William's work on Saturn, see A. F. O'D. Alexander, *The Planet Saturn: A History of Observation, Theory and Discovery* (London, 1962), chaps. 8 and 9.

270 "… by de La Lande's letter which contains his tables", RAS W.3/1.8. The tables were contained in *Connaissance des Temps* for 1791, published in 1789, 288–94.

271 RAS W.3/1.8.

272 *Chr*, 163–4.

273 RAS W.2/4, f. 2v.

274 *Chr*, 165; W.1/1, 181.

275 WH, "Account of the Discovery of a Sixth and Seventh Satellite of the Planet Saturn", *PT*, lxxx (1790), 1–20, p. 1.

276 RAS W.3/1.8, f. 27v.

277 RAS W.1/13.B.24.

278 This is discussed below in detail in "The Herschelian Revolution in Astronomy".

279 XII, 35.

280 WH, "On the Power of Penetrating into Space by Telescopes", *PT*, xc (1800), 49–85, p. 85.

281 WH, "Astronomical Observations Relating to the Sidereal Part of the Heavens", *PT*, civ (1814), 248–84, p. 275.

282 A full discussion of these discoveries, real or imagined, is to be found in A. F. O'D. Alexander, *The Planet Uranus* (ref. 153), chaps. 3 and 4.

283 WH, "A Series of Observations of the Satellites of the Georgian Planet", *PT*, cv (1815), 293–362, p. 295.

284 Caroline quotes her brother as saying, "It is impossible to make the machine act as required without a room three times as large as this", letter to John, April 1827, BL Egerton 3761.

285 *Mem*, 113.

286 XXIV, 33, follows Dreyer i, p. liii in putting this in 1815.

287 *Mem*, 124.

288 *Mem*, 123.

289 *Mem*, 127–8.

290 The only persons we know to have been allowed to look through the 40-ft are: William's wife Mary, his brother Alexander, and "another lady", who viewed Saturn on 24 September 1789 (RAS W.2/4, f. 3r); Professor Samuel Vince of Cambridge, M 2, 4 September 1799 (WH, *op. cit.* (ref. 281), 275); and a Mr Greathead and his brother, Saturn on 5 November 1799 (Dreyer, i, p. liii fn).

291 XXV, 8.

292 *Mem*, 128.

293 With its 2-ft mirrors it was significantly more powerful than William's own 20-ft, but it proved manageable, unlike William's cumbersome 40-ft.

294 Jean-Dominique Cassini, *Mémoires de l'Académie Royale des Sciences*, 1784, 333. Similarly John Brinkley, *Elements of Astronomy*, 2nd edn (London, 1819), 24, writes, "Dr. Herschel tells us …", and F. T. Schubert, *Traité d'Astronomie Théorique*, French transl. (St Petersburg, 1822), ii, 37, "M. Herschel … nous assure qu'à l'aide des grossissemens étonnans que ses téléscopes supportent, il est parvenu à voir…". In a letter to William written on 17 May 1814, Charles Blagden quotes Laplace as saying of the satellites of Uranus, that William is the only one who can see them in "le monde entier" (RAS W.1/13.B.99).

295 *Monatliche Correspondenz*, v (1802), 74.

296 *Chr*, 311.

297 *Chr*, 308–9.

298 William's detailed diary of his visit is reproduced *in extenso* (and with minor slips) in *Chronicle*, 308–11.

299 WH, "Investigations of the Powers of the Prismatic Colours to Heat and Illuminate Objects …", *PT*, xc (1800), 255–83; "Experiments on the Refrangibility of the Invisible Rays of the Sun", *ibid*, 284–92; "Experiments on the Solar, and on the Terrestrial Rays That Occasion Heat", *ibid.*, 293–326.

300 Banks to William, 9 April 1800, RAS W.1/13. B.34: "I hope you will not be affronted when I tell you that highly as I priz'd the discovery of a new Planet I consider the separation of heat from light as a discovery pregnant with more important additions to science", and he goes on to quote Count Rumford.

301 WH, "Account of the Changes That Have Happened During the Last Twenty-five Years, in the Relative Situation of Double-stars", *PT*, xciii (1803), 339–82; and "Continuation ...", *PT*, xciv (1804), 353–84.

302 By F. Savary, J. F. Encke, and John Herschel, see *SA*, 20, n. 75.

303 Banks, for example, wrote to William on 25 May 1809: "It gave me pain to hear the opinions given by the members of the Committee [of the Royal Society for publications] well versed in optical enquiries, they appeared to me unanimous in thinking that you have somehow deceived yourself in your experiments & have in consequence deduced incorrect results" (RAS W.1/13. B.51).

304 XX, 12.

305 Günther Buttmann, *The Shadow of the Telescope: A Biography of John Herschel* (London, 1974), 20.

306 XXV, 18.

307 *P'ship*, 127.

308 WH, "On the Places of 145 New Double Stars", *Memoirs of the Astronomical Society*, i (1822–25), 166–81.

309 XXV, 23–24.

Anna Christina

1 CHA, 22. In fact Maria Dorethea was born on 8 June, more than six weeks before the death of Anna Christina, so Caroline's memory is a little at fault.

Alexander

1 *CHA*, 98–99.

2 *CHA*, 25–26.

3 *Chr*, 32, states the Alexander was apprenticed in a Guild of Music, though it would be surprising if so small a town as Coppenbrügge had a Guild. George Griesbach's memoirs (in the possession of Anne Jarvis, see the biographical sketch of Sophia) make it clear he was in fact apprenticed to his uncle, and that Heinrich actually took the boy with him when he moved from Hanover to Coppenbrügge.

4 *CHA*, 107; cf. 35.

5 *CHA*, 30.

6 George Griesbach, Memoirs, 3.

7 *CHA*, 107–8. Caroline in her old age enlarges on the complaints against Griesbach that already featured in the earlier autobiography. Alexander had unselfishly put his mechanical talents at William's disposal over many decades and had been a third partner in the Herschel collaboration; but his private life had been blighted by a sense of insecurity that Caroline ascribed to his treatment at the hands of Heinrich Griesbach.

8 George Griesbach, Memoirs.

9 *CHA*, 112.

10 *CHA*, 18.

11 *CHA*, 40.

12 *CHA*, 41.

13 *CHA*, 44.

14 *CHA*, 45.

15 The musical activities of Alexander are described by James, 390–4.

16 *CHA*, 54.

17 Cited in *Mem*, 312.

18 His pupils included Dr Henry Harrington, sometime mayor of Bath and a noted amateur musician, and Matthew Patton,

proprietor of a musical establishment there (Ewing Collection Rd 87/151, Glasgow University Library).

19 According to John Marsh, manuscript memoirs, ix, 754 [Cambridge University Library, Add MS 7757], Alexander "was a true German; being a strict timist, but scouting the more delicate refinements of Italy; in consequence of which, whenever Tenducci sang at any concert at Bath, he and Herschel were always sparring, as whenever the former wished to lengthen a note, or vary a little from the strict time, when the expression of the sentiment seemed to require it, which he used to signify to the band with a motion of his hand, Herschel would always keep on without varying an iota but keeping rigidly to the time, saying there was no pause or adagio marked".

20 James, 690.

21 We learn of Alexander's involvement in the payments to Anna through the one letter dictated by her that survives (see the biographical sketch of Isaac and Anna), and through the letter of William to Alexander, 10 March 1785 (RAS W.1/9), where he confirms he is forwarding Alexander's money to Anna.

22 *CHA*, 51.

23 Caroline to Margaret Herschel, letter of 31 July 1841, BL Egerton 3762.

24 "Anecdotes from John F. Herschel's, recorded by our uncle James Stewart's handwriting", manuscript in the Herschel Family Archives, 16.

25 *CHA*, 52.

26 *CHA*, 129.

27 *CHA*, 128.

28 *CHA*, 127. Angus Armitage, *William Herschel* (London, 1962), 41, describes the procedure for making a mirror in Robert Smith's *Opticks* (William's guide in such matters), as follows: "Circular brass gauges were first cut to the curvature prescribed for the speculum. These were employed in turning to a true figure a pewter pattern which, in its turn, served to shape a mould of sand into which the molten speculum metal was poured. There followed the laborious process of grinding and polishing the casting

till it received the precise spherical or paraboloidal figure intended."

29 *CHA*, 127–8.

30 *CHA*, 55.

31 *CHA*, 62.

32 *CHA*, 57.

33 RAS W.5/12.1, expt 202.

34 RAS W.2/1.4.

35 Marsh, manuscript memoirs (ref. 19), ix, 753–4, tells of sitting next to William at supper in May 1782. "... entering into some discourse with him upon astronomy, which he then applied to much more than music, he told me of his being then at work upon a mirror for a large telescope, of the magnifying powers of which he was very sanguine in his hopes, and which proved to be the one which soon afterwards brought him to the notice of his majesty, and occasioned his removal to Windsor. His sister and his brother, who played the principal violoncello at Bath, was as fond of astronomy as himself and all used to sit up, star-gazing, in the coldest frosty nights."

36 "Alexander's 5 feet Gregorian brass tube 9 inch motion in brass was sold (I know not to whom) perhaps for a trifle his valuable clockmakers tools went for old iron", Caroline to John, 18 April 1832, BL Egerton 3761.

37 George III knew of Alexander and enquired after him from William, who wrote to Caroline on 26 May 1782, "Tell Alexander that everything looks very likely as if I were to stay here. The King enquired after him...", RAS W.1/8. It seems that the King, no doubt remembering Jacob's musical performance at Court, had previously asked George Griesbach about William's brothers, and would then have been told about Alexander: "His Majesty enquired likewise what brothers he had and other circumstances", letter of Watson to Banks, 27 March 1782, Dawson Turner Collection, ii, 108. On 4 April, Watson told Banks, "His Majesty enquired after Mr Griesbach's <u>Uncles</u>; being informed that my friend has a Brother, who is likewise very ingenious. He plays on the Violoncello", *ibid.*, 117–20.

38 When he was in Bath out of season, however, he did undertake engagements there (and at Wells). Kenneth James has located advertisements that show that Alexander took part in concerts, mostly in Bath garden parade, in 1787 (Aug, Sept), 1788 (May, Aug), 1789 (Aug), 1790 (May, Aug), 1791 (May, June), 1796 (June), 1798 (June, Aug), and 1799 (May, June).

39 The letter from Dietrich is appended to one dictated to him by Anna and dating from July or August 1782, in response to the news of William's royal appointment; that from Jacob is dated 30 December 1782. Both are lost, but translations by Constance Lubbock survive in the Herschel Family Archives.

40 *CHA*, 68.

41 Translation by Constance Lubbock, in the Herschel Family Archives.

42 From the church register, now in the County Archives at Taunton. Alexander's marriage to "Mrs Smith" is reported in the *Bath Chronicle* for 7 August 1783: "Thursday last was married at Walcot Church Mr Alexander Herschel, to Mrs Smith, both of this city".

43 *CHA*, 68–69.

44 *CHA*, 73.

45 More exactly, with his usual magnification of 157, the field of view was 15′4″, WH, "Catalogue of One Thousand New Nebulae and Clusters of Stars", *PT*, lxxvi (1786), 457–99, p. 457.

46 Bennett, 86.

47 National Maritime Museum, Greenwich, MS/79/118. The letters are printed in full in MH, "Alexander Herschel: The Forgotten Partner", *JHA*, xxxv (2004), 387–420.

48 *CHA*, 128.

49 RAS W.2/1.7.

50 Aubert to William, 19 October 1786, RAS W.1/13.A.26.

51 *CHA*, 89.

52 See, among innumerable examples, Caroline's entry for 16 December 1791 in RAS C.1/1.4.

53 "Anecdotes" (ref. 24), 9–10.

54 Because this is the period for which Caroline destroyed her memoirs (the surviving ones make no mention of Alexander's making her this clock), and because this is the period when she had most need of it.

55 Watson to William, RAS W.1/13.W.30.

56 Jonathan Betts suggests this name might have been a play on that of John Monk, the principal maker of such clocks at the time.

57 It was by the great clockmaker John Shelton, and had been presented to William in October 1786 by Alexander Aubert (letter from Aubert to William, 19 October 1786, RAS W.1/A.26).

58 *Mem*, 207. The clock was auctioned in 1958 as Lot 459 in the Sotheby's Herschel sale, when it was described as having a brass face and a wooden case, and being 3ft 10½ inches high. W. H. Steavenson had earlier reported that the case was painted black, and that the pendulum was missing ("A Peep into Herschel's Workshop", *Transactions of the Optical Society*, xxvi (1924–25), 210–37, p. 237). It was sold, along with two 1785 letters from Alexander to William, for the princely sum of five pounds; sadly, the present whereabouts of the clock cannot be ascertained.

59 Caroline to John, 18 April 1832, cited above, ref. 36.

60 William to Alexander, 10 March 1785, RAS W.1/9.3. A journeyman was a workman who had completed his apprenticeship.

61 *CHA*, 75.

62 The 20-ft came into service on 23 October 1783, less than three months after Alexander's wedding, and Caroline says that when her brother first visited Datchet he was already married.

63 For full details see MH, "Herschel's 40ft Reflector: Funding and Functions", *JHA*, xxxiv (2003), 1–32.

64 On 11 June 1784, for example, William recorded that his instrument had been disturbed in showing a nebula to Alexander, RAS W.2/1.9. In 1785 William wrote to Alexander in anticipation of his visit (ref. 60). From 3 July to 16 August 1786, William and Alexander were away delivering to Göttingen one of the 10-ft reflectors William had made for the

King; on 19 October Alexander Aubert wrote to William presenting him with a regulator by Shelton and adding: "I hope your brother is not gone and that the clock gets down time enough for him to put it up for you", RAS W.1/13.A.26; *Chr*, 181. In 1787, however, Alexander "came only for a short time to give his brother [Jacob] the meeting, Mrs H. being too ill to be left alone" (*Chr*, 93). Alexander's wife died the following February, so that he was free again to help William, who notes on 9 September 1788: "My brother Alexander saw the satellites [of Saturn]", W.2/1.12.

65   XI, 14.

66   Letters forming part of RAS W.1/13.

67   According to Constance Lubbock, "Schroeter accepted the offer [of a 7-ft by Alexander for 22 guineas] and was so well pleased with the purchase that he procured an order for a similar telescope from Bode at Berlin, and several more commissions for William's brother", XI, 16. Yet she herself notes in her summary of the Schröter–William letters that "strangely" there is no acknowledgement by Schröter of receipt of the 7-ft mirrors, so it is puzzling to know the basis for this assertion.

68   For these documents see John Tracy Spaight, "Alexander Herschel as Telescope Maker", *JHA*, xxxiv (2003), 95–96.

69   William's letter of 10 March 1785 (RAS W.1/9.2) is addressed to 19 New King Street, but his letter of 7 February 1788 (RAS W.1/9.3) is addressed to 3 Margarett's Place, near Walcot Parade, Bath. In 1800 Alexander's address is listed as 3 Margaret's Hill, in the *Bath Directory* for that year.

70   "Anecdotes" (ref. 24), 15.

71   Alexander was to make a further visit to Hanover before the death of Anna in November 1789, for in an undated letter (RAS W.1/9.5) William sends his best wishes to his mother.

72   William to Caroline, 1 August 1786, RAS W.1/8.

73   Her complaints are aired in *CHA*, 86.

74   *CHA*, 93. William's letter of condolence (ref. 69) is dated 7 February. She was buried at All Saints', Weston, Bath on 10 February.

75   "Caroline destroyed every page of her Journals which contained any reference to this period of her life", XIII, 11.

76   RAS W.2/1.12.

77   A description and discussion of the Greenwich artefacts is given by Jonathan Betts in an appendix to MH, "Alexander Herschel" (ref. 47).

78   RAS W.1/8.18.

79   See MH, "Herschel's 40ft Reflector" (ref. 63).

80   *Mem*, 113.

81   Caroline to John Herschel, 14 July 1823, BL Egerton 3762.

82   XXIV, 30.

83   *Chr*, 343.

84   *Chr*, 344.

85   *Chr*, 345.

86   British Library microfilm M/588(4).

87   *Chr*, 346.

88   *Chr*, 346–7. He arrived on 15 September, RAS C.4/3, p. 30.

89   RAS C.4/3, p. 30.

90   *Chr*, 346–7. The date of death is from the register of the Aegidienkirche, Hanover.

91   An article on "Die Grabinschriften der Gartenmeinde in Hannover" in the *Zeitschrift für niedersächsische Kirchengeschichte* for 1939 states that A. Herschel was buried in the Gartenfriedhof in 1821, and this must surely be Alexander. His grave has not been located, but this may be because stones were stolen from the graveyard in the aftermath of the Second World War.

92   "There is one [stone] put worth 18 pence", Caroline to Margaret Herschel, 4 February 1843, BL Egerton 3762.

93   Caroline to John, 4 June 1831, BL Egerton 3761.

94   BL Egerton 3761.

Maria Dorethea

1   CHA, 15, 97.

Caroline

1 Caroline to John, 21 August 1838, BL Egerton 3762.
2 *CHA*, 22.
3 *P'ship*, 158, n. 52.
4 *CHA*, 47.
5 *CHA*, 25.
6 *CHA*, 102.
7 *CHA*, 7.
8 "I never could remember the multiplication table, but was obliged to carry always a copy of it about me", Caroline to John, 1 September 1840, BL Egerton 3762.
9 *Mem*, 387.
10 *CHA*, 37.
11 *CHA*, 34.
12 *CHA*, 34.
13 Caroline to John, 4 June 1831, BL Egerton 3761: "Six years ago I had a vault built in the spot where my parents rest. The ground is mine *auf ewig*."
14 Caroline to John, 9 January 1833, *ibid.*: she has bought the grave of her father and mother and paid for a stone for herself.
15 "Beneath this Stone are deposited the remains of Caroline Herschel M.R.I.A. & A.S.L. Who died this ... month 184. aged &c. In or near this place Her Father Isaac Herschel was buried March 25, 1767. Aged 60 years, 2 months and 17 days", dated by Caroline 26 July 1844, BL microfilm M/588(4). Caroline takes pride in her election as Member of the Royal Irish Academy and of the Astronomical Society of London, although by 1844 the latter institution had for thirteen years been The Royal Astronomical Society.
16 The second inscription (translated into German) is to be seen on her tomb to this day. Her English original draft reads: "Here rest the earthly remains of Caroline Herschel Born at Hanover 16th March 1750 Died .... The gaze of the deceased while here below, was turned towards the starry heavens; her own discovery of comets and her share in the immortal labours of her brother William Herschel will testify hereof to future generations. The Royal Irish Academy

of Dublin and the Royal Astronomical Society of London counted her among their members. At the age of ... years ... months ... days she fell asleep in the calm and cheerful possession of all her powers of mind, following to a better world her father Isaac Herschel who after attaining the age of 60 years 2 months 17 days was buried in this place 25th March 1767", *ibid.* Constance Lubbock, evidently unaware of the original English version, provides a translation, *Chr*, 382.
17 *CHA*, 108.
18 *CHA*, 107.
19 *CHA*, 34.
20 Once again, Caroline's complaints refer to the whole of her life and are by no means restricted to her upbringing. Her repeated criticisms of the fifty years she spent at the beck and call of William deserve more attention than they have received.
21 *CHA*, 110.
22 *Ibid.*
23 *CHA*, 37–38.
24 *CHA*, 36.
25 *CHA*, 36.
26 *Ibid.*
27 *Ibid.*
28 *CHA*, 37.
29 *CHA*, 114.
30 *CHA*, 39.
31 Abigail, a lady's maid, from the name of a character in a seventeenth-century play.
32 *CHA*, 114.
33 *CHA*, 41.
34 *CHA*, 41–42.
35 Madam Beckedorff, who later became a lady-in-waiting to Queen Charlotte, see below.
36 *CHA*, 42.
37 *CHA*, 42.
38 *CHA*, 43–44.
39 *CHA*, 44.
40 *CHA*, 44.
41 *CHA*, 44–45.
42 *CHA*, 44.
43 *CHA*, 45.

44 *CHA*, 45.

45 *CHA*, 46.

46 Caroline to Margaret Herschel, 24 September 1838, BL Egerton 3762.

47 *CHA*, 47.

48 *CHA*, 47, 116.

49 *CHA*, 47.

50 *CHA*, 47.

51 *CHA*, 47.

52 The payments feature in the one letter from Anna that survives (as dictated to Dietrich, and translated by Constance Lubbock, see the biographical sketch of Isaac and Anna). And in Jacob's letter to William of 27 February 1786 (*ibid.*) he reports that Anna "thanks you much for sending the 10 guineas, which she received duly".

53 *CHA*, 119.

54 *CHA*, 118.

55 *CHA*, 49.

56 *CHA*, 120.

57 *CHA*, 123.

58 *CHA*, 119.

59 *CHA*, 50, 119.

60 *CHA*, 50.

61 *CHA*, 120.

62 *CHA*, 120.

63 *CHA*, 120.

64 *CHA*, 120.

65 *CHA*, 120.

66 *CHA*, 120.

67 *CHA*, 121.

68 *CHA*, 121.

69 *CHA*, 121.

70 *CHA*, 123.

71 *CHA*, 122.

72 See fn. to II, 4.

73 *CHA*, 52.

74 *CHA*, 55, 128.

75 *CHA*, 129.

76 *CHA*, 53, 123–6.

77 It features at length in her second autobiography.

78 *CHA*, 124.

79 *CHA*, 124.

80 *CHA*, 124.

81 The Pantheon was the building that brought its architect James Wyatt (1746–1813) to prominence. It has been described as "a sort of indoor Vauxhall". In 1791 it was adapted for opera, but it burned down the following year. Its site is now occupied by the famous store of Marks & Spencer's.

82 *CHA*, 125.

83 *CHA*, 126.

84 *CHA*, 127.

85 *CHA*, 57.

86 *CHA*, 29.

87 *P'ship*, 46.

88 *P'ship*, 45.

89 *CHA*, 62.

90 *CHA*, 65.

91 *CHA*, 68.

92 *CHA*, 71.

93 *CHA*, 73.

94 *CHA*, 71.

95 RAS W.4/1.3, 240.

96 *CHA*, 71.

97 In the Historisches Museum. See Margaret Bullard, "My small Newtonian sweeper — where is it now?", *Notes and Records of the Royal Society of London*, xlii (1988), 139–48.

98 RAS C.1/1.1, 4.

99 *CHA*, 71–73.

100 MH, "Caroline Herschel as Observer", *JHA*, xxxvi (2005), 373–406; "Caroline Herschel's Catalogue of Nebulae", *JHA*, xxxvii (2006), 251–5; "In Caroline Herschel's Footsteps", *Sky & Telescope*, cxiv/2 (August, 2007), 59–62. I conclude that Caroline is to be credited with the discovery (or independent rediscovery) of 14 nebulae, a remarkable achievement under the circumstances, but one that she downplayed in the light of the catalogues of 2510 nebulae published by her brother.

101 Two observations of a comet do not define its orbit; a third is required. However, Brian Marsden discusses possible orbits in the light of various plausible assumptions made in lieu of a third observation, MH, "Caroline Herschel as Observer" (ref. 100), Appendix 2.

102 Barthélmy Faujas-de-St-Fond, *Voyage en Angleterre, en Écosse et aux îles Hébrides: ayant pour objet les sciences, les arts, l'histoire*

naturelle et les moeurs avec la description mineralogique du pays de Newcastle des montagnes du Derbyshire, des environs d'Edinburgh, de Glasgow, de Perth, de S. Andrews, du duche d'Inverary et de les grotte de Fingal (2 vols, Paris, 1797), i, 74–76, 81. William B. Ashworth, Jr, "Faujas-de-Saint-Fond Visits the Herschels at Datchet", *JHA*, xxxiv (2003), 321–4.

103 Namely, Dreyer.

104 Caroline to Charles Blagden, 2 August 1786, RAS C.1/3.1.

105 Comment by Fanny Burney, *Chr*, 169.

106 Caroline to Mary Herschel, 14 October 1824, BL Egerton 3761.

107 RAS W.1/5.2(i).

108 WH, "An Account of Three Volcanos in the Moon", *PT*, lxxvii (1787), 229–32. Caroline examined the Moon in the search for "luminous spots" on 17, 19 and 20 March 1790 (RAS C.1/1.2) and William on 18 March (RAS W.3/1.4) but there is no reason stated for this flurry of interest. A month later Caroline repeated the exercise on two nights but again without success. She looked again on 14 March, 14 April and 7 October 1793, 4 January ("I see a very bright spot"), 3 and 22 May, 30 June and 29 October 1794, and 23 January 1795 (RAS C.1/1.4).

109 RAS C.3/2.3.

110 Caroline to Sir Joseph Banks, 17 August 1797, *Mem*, 94–95. For Maskelyne's gift to Caroline of a field-glass and binoculars, see *Chr*, 297.

111 Caroline to Nevil Maskelyne, September 1798, *Chr*, 257.

112 Karl Seyffer to Caroline, 10 May [?1793], *Mem*, 92.

113 *P'ship*, 171, ref. 48. Lalande also nominated William and it was not thought right to give prizes to members of the same family.

114 "Extracts from a daybook kept during the years 1797 & 1821", BL microfilm M/588(4).

115 BL microfilm M/588(4).

116 Caroline to John, 4 May 1843, BL Egerton 3762.

117 Caroline to Mary Herschel, 6 September 1833, BL Egerton 3761.

118 *Chr*, 296.

119 *Mem*, 98–99.

120 Caroline to Margaret Herschel, February 1843, BL Egerton 3762.

121 *P'ship*, 115.

122 *Mem*, 101.

123 See her preface to RAS W.2/3.

124 RAS C.3/2. "Completed the Cat. of stars in 1818", Caroline's note concerning her despatch to John of this and other documents, BL microfilm M/588(4).

125 *Mem*, 105.

126 *Mem*, 105.

127 *Mem*, 106.

128 Caroline to Mary, 14 October 1824, BL Egerton 3761.

129 *Mem*, 116.

130 *Mem*, 136.

131 IV, 3.

132 XXIII, 7.

133 *Mem*, 122–3.

134 Herschel/M 1090, 1, Harry Ransom Library, Humanities Research Center, University of Texas at Austin.

135 Caroline to John, 18 April 1832, BL Egerton 3761.

136 Caroline to John, 8 August 1826, BL Egerton 3761.

137 Caroline to Mary Herschel, 5 April 1840, BL Egerton 3762.

138 John to Sir David Smith, 25 September 1822, Royal Society Library, HS 19.37.

139 Caroline to John, 27 February 1823, BL Egerton 3761.

140 "It will now be right to mention more particularly the modifications I have introduced into my father's method of sweeping, — modifications rendered necessary by the loss of my aunt, Miss CAROLINE HERSCHEL's personal assistance, on whom the task of reading and registering the Polar distances and Right Ascensions of objects, writing down the remarks and descriptions, warning the observer of expected stars, and finally reducing and calculating the whole, used invariably to devolve. Unsupported by such aid, I am under the necessity of recording the observations myself; an inconvenience of the worst kind, not only as it diminishes at least

by one half, the number of objects that can be taken, but because the frequent admission of extraneous light into the eye is fatal to observations of the fainter nebulae." John Herschel, "Observations of Nebulae and Clusters ...", *PT*, cxxiii (1833), 359–506, p. 461.

141 Cited by Agnes M. Clerke, *The Herschels and Modern Astronomy* (London, 1895), 132.

142 Caroline to John, 3 February 1829: "I am too confused at present from the effects of a cold in the head to give you a proper idea of my Motherly feelings towards you ...", BL Egerton 3761.

143 Caroline to P. Stewart, 25 May 1835, BL Egerton 3762.

144 Caroline to Margaret Herschel, 21 June 1841, BL Egerton 3762 (mislocated in file).

145 Caroline to John, 21 August 1838, BL Egerton 3762: 6475 thalers. Caroline to John, 21 June 1841, *ibid*.: 3977 thalers 28 groschen plus 3720 thalers, this being her third calculation.

146 *P'ship*, 147.

147 Caroline to John, autumn 1841, BL Egerton 3762.

148 Caroline to John, 21 August 1838, BL Egerton 3762.

149 Caroline to John, 4 May 1843, BL Egerton 3762.

150 Caroline's daybook, 16 July 1839, *Mem*, 306.

151 Caroline's daybook, 25 July 1839, *Mem*, 307.

152 Caroline to John, 11 September 1834, BL Egerton 3762.

153 John to Caroline, 22 February 1835, *Mem*, 270.

154 Caroline to John, 4 August 1842, BL Egerton 3762

155 Caroline to John, 4 June 1844, BL Egerton 3762.

156 Translated from the German in *Mem*, 346.

Frantz Johann

1 The dates cited by Isaac, *CHA*, 98, are for some reason erroneous, see *ibid*., n. 2. He was buried on the 29th.

2 *CHA*, 22.

Dietrich

1 *CHA*, 33 and 111.
2 *CHA*, 41.
3 *CHA*, 43 and 115.
4 *CHA*, 43 and 115.
5 *CHA*, 45, 46 and 116.
6 *CHA*, 116; *cf.* 46.
7 *CHA*, 46.
8 *CHA*, 41; *P'ship*, 41.
9 *CHA*, 56–57, 131–3.
10 *CHA*, 57.
11 VII, 22.
12 "Memorandums".
13 "I wish my uncle had not confined himself to a mere catalogue of insects, but had told us a little of their habits", John Herschel to Caroline, 18 April 1825,

Mem, 188–9.
14 RAS W.5/12.1.
15 VII, 22 recounts that "Dietrich had only to express a wish, whether for a microscope, or to have the mirror of his telescope polished, — 'five minutes in your hands, dear brother' he wrote, 'would do', — or a request laid before Sir Joseph Banks for permission to get some entomological specimens from Egypt forwarded under cover to the Royal Society — and William's assistance was at once cheerfully given".

16 *Mem*, 70–71.
17 Information from Kuno von Bierberstein, a distant relative.
18 *CHA*, 59. Mr Reif became landlord to the

Herschels at Michaelmas 1771 (*CHA*, 47), previously to which they had moved apartments on an almost annual basis. The name of Dietrich's wife, and the date of their marriage, were found in the register of the Hanover Schlosskirche by Arndt Latusseck. She was born on 16 January 1760 (register of the Aegidienkirche). Catharina was to die on 1 December 1846 at the age of 86 years and 10 months (register of the Schlosskirche).

19 Information from the Schlosskirche register.

20 Translation by Constance Lubbock of a letter dictated by Anna to Dietrich (to which Dietrich added a message of his own) in the Herschel Family Archives.

21 RAS W.1/8.

22 VII, 23.

23 *Ibid.*

24 That Knipping was (supposedly) American is mentioned in the letters from Caroline to Margaret Herschel, *c.* February 1840, and to John Herschel, 29 November 1840, BL Egerton 3762. However, information from (somewhat contradictory) printed sources supplied by Kuno von Bierberstein states that Knipping was born in "Hemeringen" (possibly the one near Hamelm) on 21 January 1760, the son of Johann Friedrick Knipping and his wife Charlotte Louise, and studied law at Göttingen. It seems therefore that he was German by birth. However, he then became a businessman at Charlestown, USA, before establishing himself at Bremen with his wife.

25 *Chr*, 316. Caroline gives Knipping the title Amptmann, civil servant, in a letter to Patrick (otherwise Peter) Stewart, brother-in-law of John Herschel, 25 May 1835 (*Mem*, 277–8).

26 XXII, 20.

27 *Chr*, 319.

28 *Chr*, 218.

29 *Chr*, 320.

30 *Mem*, 22.

31 *Mem*, 116.

32 "During the four years — between 1808 and 1813 — my brother Dietrerich remained in England, I spared him out of my small income each year £40", Caroline

Herschel, "Historycal Memorandums of the Years from 1722 to &c &c &c", Harry Ransom Library, University of Texas.

33 *Mem*, 136.

34 *Mem*, 136.

35 *Mem*, 221.

36 *P'ship*, 129.

37 *Mem*, 136.

38 Information supplied from printed sources by Kuno von Bierberstein.

39 Caroline to Margaret Herschel (John's wife), 14 October 1824, BL Egerton 3761. In a letter to John, 18 April 1832, *ibid.*, Caroline says that when she was still in England, Dietrich informed her of the "deranged" affairs of his son-in-law.

40 "... you remember I parted with my little property before I left England (against your good advice) because I thought at that time I should not live a 12 month and wished to enable my Brother to save the Family of his 2d daughter with that sum from ruin, but it was of no avail, and her husband who was one of the first Phisicians here, has now been 3 years in a mad house and Madam Richter with her 4 Children were settled in the Country...", Caroline to John Herschel, 8 August 1826, BL Egerton 3761. "For in consequence of a letter I received shortly before I left England in which my Brother acquainted me with the derranged affairs of his son in law Dr Richter ... I made him by return of the post the offer of my whole property (which perhaps you know) was 500£ in the 3pct. It was accepted with interest and all, without making any further mention of it either by letter or word of mouth, except when in my presence boasting of his new independency he sometimes would acknowledge I had something contributed towards it." Caroline to John, 18 April 1832, BL Egerton 3761.

41 *P'ship*, 131–2. Caroline to Margaret Herschel, 12 November 1822, BL Egerton 3761.

42 Caroline to John, 25 September 1827, BL Egerton 3761.

43 *Mem*, 218.

44 Caroline to Margaret Herschel, 14 October 1824, BL Egerton 3761, says that Richter is "a Brother of the divorced husband of

the late Mrs Quaintin who has this long while been in a privat madhouse", but that he is "one of our best Phisicians here who is still at <u>Intervals</u> in good practice". Richter was to die in February 1832 "and can molest his wife & Family no longer" (Caroline to John, 18 April 1832, BL Egerton 3761).

45 Caroline, writing to Margaret Herschel on 14 October 1824 (BL Egerton 3761), says that they are "a happy Couple. Dr G is pretty far advanced in years but did not marrie a young wife without having the means to provide well for her". Groskopff was to prove a valuable friend to Caroline in the years to come.

46 See for example *Mem*, 318. Groskopff was alive in March 1841 (*Mem*, 318), but it seems

he predeceased Caroline, for in the event John is said to have been her executor (*Mem*, 346). Groskopff's widow Caroline was still alive in June 1864 (*Mem*, 352).

47 Lubbock illustrates this with quotations from his letters, *Chr*, 71.

48 Caroline to John, 20 September 1825, BL Egerton 3761.

49 Caroline to John, 8 August 1826, BL Egerton 3761.

50 Caroline to Mary Herschel, 1 November 1826, BL Egerton 3761.

51 Caroline to John, 24 December 1826, BL Egerton 3761.

52 Caroline to John, 22 January 1827, BL Egerton 3761; register of the Neustaedter Hof- und Stadtkirche, Hanover.

The Herschelian Revolution in Astronomy

1 XI, 28, from Charlotte Papendiek, *Court and Private Life in the Time of Queen Charlotte: being the journals of Mrs. Papendiek* (London, 1887). Mrs Papendiek's father held the lease of the house at Slough immediately before William.

2 The classic article on William's telescopes is Bennett. For further information, see "A Compendium of All Known William Herschel Telescopes", by Andreas Maurer, *Journal of the Antique Telescope Society*, no. 14 (1998), 4–15, and John Tracy Spaight, "'For the Good of Astronomy': The Manufacture, Sale and Distant Use of William Herschel's Telescopes", *JHA*, xxxv (2004), 45–69.

3 Nevil Maskelyne to William, 21 February 1789, RAS W.1/13.M.40.

4 Nevil Maskelyne to William, 9 June 1788, RAS W.1/13.M.35.

5 The chair is shown in the painting by the Rev. Thomas Rackett, and is mentioned by John Smeaton in his letter to John Michell, 4 November 1785, copy in RAS MS Radcliffe Hornsby 78.

6 On this see Bennett, 93–95.

7 Bennett, 95–97.

8 RAS W.2/2.5, f. 52v.

9 RAS W.1/4; 1/1, p. 290.

10 *Monatliche Correspondenz*, v (1802), 74.

11 WH, "On the Proper Motion of the Sun and Solar System", *PT*, lxxiii (1783), 247–83, pp. 249–50.

12 WH, "Catalogue of Double Stars", *PT*, lxxii (1782), 112–62.

13 WH, "Catalogue of Double Stars", *PT*, lxxv (1785), 40–126. Over the decades he continued from time to time to come across a double star, and at the very end of his life he and Caroline assembled a list as a token offering to the newly-formed Astronomical Society of London: WH, "On the Places of 145 New Double Stars", *Memoirs of the Astronomical Society*, i (1822–25), 166–81.

14 RAS W.4/1.1, f. 7.

15 For further information see MH, "William Herschel's Early Investigations of Nebulae", *JHA*, x (1980), 165–76 [= *SA*, 125–36].

16 RAS W.4/1.3, f. 224.

17 MH, "Caroline Herschel as Observer", *JHA*, xxxvi (2005), 373–406.

18 RAS W.2/1.7, f. 4.

19 MH, "Unfinished Business: William Herschel's Sweeps for Nebulae", *History of Science*,

xliii (2005), 305–20. On the inside front cover of the first of seven books of original records of sweeps (Royal Society MS 272), William notes: "Before these sweeps in the meridian were made, I had made 45 in the parallel. See Journal. Those 45 were made by swinging the suspended telescope backwards and forwards."

20 WH, "Catalogue of One Thousand New Nebulae and Clusters of Stars", *PT*, lxxvi (1786), 457–99.

21 WH, "Catalogue of a Second Thousand of New Nebulae and Clusters of Stars", *PT*, lxxix (1789), 212–55.

22 4 March 1796: "About 13′ preceding and 5 or 6′ north of the Georgian Planet [Uranus] is a nebula...", RAS W.2/1.13. The nebula became I.272 in the catalogues of nebulae and clusters.

23 *P'ship*, 115.

24 WH, *op. cit.* (ref. 20), 457.

25 WH, "Catalogue of 500 New Nebulae, Nebulous Stars, Planetary Nebulae, and Clusters of Stars", *PT*, xcii (1802), 477–528.

26 Royal Society L&P XII, 34.

27 *Mem*, 108.

28 They appear as III.979, 980 and 981 (26 September) and II.908 and 909 and III.982 and 983 (30 September).

29 III.984 (observed on 17 November 1784) and II.910 and III.985 (24 March 1791).

30 WH, "Account of Some Observations Tending to Investigate the Construction of the Heavens", *PT*, lxxiv (1784), 437–51 [= *Construction*, 71–82]; "On the Construction of the Heavens", *PT*, lxxv (1785), 213–66 [in part = *Construction*, 82–106].

31 On the early history of variable stars, see MH, "Novae and Variables from Tycho to Bullialdus", *Sudhoffs Archiv*, lxi (1977), 195–204 [= *SA*, 22–28].

32 On the work of Goodricke and Pigott, see MH, "Goodricke, Pigott and the Quest for Variable Stars", *JHA*, x (1979), 23–41 [= *SA*, 37–55].

33 E. C. Pickering, in *Annals of the Observatory of Harvard College*, xxiii (1890), 231, cited by Dreyer, i, p. xliii.

34 The clock is illustrated on p. 138 of MH (ed.), *The Cambridge Illustrated History of Astronomy* (Cambridge, 1997).

35 MH, "Newton, Providence and the Universe of Stars", *JHA*, viii (1977), 77–101 [= *SA*, 71–95]; MH, "Stukeley's Cosmology and the Newtonian Origins of Olbers's Paradox", *JHA*, xvi (1985), 77–112.

36 H. G. Alexander (ed.), *The Leibniz–Clarke Correspondence* (Manchester, 1956), 11–12.

37 See *SA*, 101–23 for Thomas Wright of Durham and J. H. Lambert.

38 In *Philosophical Transactions* his most extended statement of this conviction occurs in "On the Nature and Construction of the Sun and Fixed Stars" (lxxxv (1795), 46–72), where he argues that not only the Moon and the various planets and their satellites, but even "the sun is richly stored with inhabitants" (p. 68).

39 The best account is still that of Angus Armitage, *William Herschel* (London, 1962), chap. 3. See also A. F. O'D. Alexander, *The Planet Uranus: A History of Observation, Theory and Discovery* (London, 1965), chap. 1.

40 The modern value is about 14.5. On William's discovery of satellites, genuine and otherwise, see *ibid.*, chaps. 3 and 4.

41 A. F. O'D. Alexander, *The Planet Saturn: A History of Observation, Theory and Discovery* (London, 1962), chaps. 8 and 9.

42 RAS W.3/1.4 contains all William's observations of the Moon. The first mention of his interest in possible volcanoes on the Moon occurs on 27 July 1780. In the autumn of 1780, he thought he had found evidence of lava flows, and on 4 May 1783 "I perceived in the dark part of the moon a very luminous spot", which a visitor confirmed without prompting and which William later reckoned as his first volcano. He continued to examine the Moon from time to time, and on 19 April 1787 saw what he took to be his third volcano. The following night "The volcano burns with greater violence", and he was now sufficiently certain of his evidence to send a short paper on "An Account of Three Volcanoes in the Moon" (*PT*, lxxvii (1787), 229–32), and to offer to show the object to the King

(letter to "Mr Ernest", 20 May 1787, RAS W.1/1). The news was seen by the Royal Society as of such "brilliancy" that special arrangements were made for its rapid publication (letter of Charles Blagden to William, 11 May 1787, RAS W.1/13. B.86). Thereafter the only notable claim by William in this regard concerns his observations of the eclipsed Moon on 22 October 1790, when "I perceived many bright red points in several parts of the Moon.... If all the small red spots should be volcanos there is indeed a great number of them, for I suppose that I saw perhaps 150 of them" (RAS W.3/1.4). Both he and Caroline (see "Caroline", ref. 108) would examine the Moon a number of times in later years, but could find no sign of volcanic activity.

43 WH, "On the Construction of the Heavens" (ref. 30, 1785), 213.

44 Michael Hoskin and David Dewhirst, "William Herschel and the Prehistory of Stellar Spectroscopy", *JHA*, xxxvii (2006), 393–403.

45 WH, *op. cit.* (ref. 38), 68.

46 Edmond Halley, "Considerations on the Change of the Latitudes of Some of the Principal Fixt Stars", *PT*, xxx (1717–19), 736–8.

47 James Ferguson, *Astronomy Explained upon Sir Isaac Newton's Principles*, 2nd edn (London, 1757), 237.

48 For a discussion of the background to William's first paper on the solar motion (ref. 11) and an analysis of his argument, see MH, "Herschel's Determination of the Solar Apex", *JHA*, xi (1780), 153–63 [= *SA*, 56–66].

49 WH, "On the Direction and Velocity of the Motion of the Sun, and Solar System", *PT*, xcv (1805), 233–56; "On the Quantity and Velocity of the Solar Motion", *PT*, xcvi (1806), 205–37. These papers are discussed in *Construction*, 55–59.

50 MH, "Newton, Providence and the Universe of Stars" (ref. 35), 96.

51 John Michell, "An Enquiry into the Probable Parallax and Magnitude of the Fixed Stars", *PT*, lvii (1767), 234–64; "On the Means of Discovering the Distance, Magnitude etc. of the Fixed Stars", *PT*,

lxxiv (1784), 35–57.

52 WH, "Account of the Changes That Have Happened, During the Last Twenty-five Years, in the Relative Situation of Double Stars", *PT*, xciii (1803), 339–82; "Continuation of an Account of the Changes That Have Happened in the Relative Situation of Double Stars", *PT*, xciv (1804), 353–84.

53 *SA*, 15.

54 WH, "Astronomical Observations Relating to the Construction of the Heavens", *PT*, ci (1811), 269–336, p. 269.

55 Known today as NGC 7009, the Saturn Nebula.

56 See *SA*, 136.

57 MH, "William Herschel's Early Investigations of Nebulae" (ref. 15), 166–9 [= *SA*, 126–9].

58 WH, *op. cit.* (ref. 30, 1784).

59 See ref. 37.

60 WH, *op. cit.* (ref. 30, 1785).

61 WH, "Astronomical Observations and Experiments Tending to Investigate the Local Arrangement of the Celestial Bodies in Space", *PT*, cvii (1817), 302–31, p. 326: "By these observations it appears that the utmost stretch of the space-penetrating power of the 20 feet telescope could not fathom the Profundity of the milky way...." WH, "Astronomical Observations and Experiments", *PT*, cviii (1818), 429–70, section V: "... the milky way ... is fathomless."

62 RAS W.4/1.7, ff. 642–3.

63 RAS W.2/1.9, f. 29r.

64 Introductory remarks to WH, *op. cit.* (ref. 21).

65 *Ibid*, 226.

66 WH, "On Nebulous Stars, Properly So Called", *PT*, lxxxi (1791), 71–88 [= *Construction*, 118–29], 82.

67 WH, "Astronomical Observations Relating to the Sidereal Part of the Heavens", *PT*, civ (1814), 248–84, p. 283.

68 WH, "Astronomical Observations and Experiments" (ref. 61, 1818), 463.

69 WH, *opera cit.* (refs 54, 67).

70 WH, *op. cit.* (ref. 54), 271.

71 WH, *opera cit.* (ref. 61).

72 John Herschel, "Observations of Nebulae and

Clusters", *PT*, cxxiii (1833), 359–506.

73 John Herschel, *Results of Observations Made ... at the Cape of Good Hope* (London, 1847).

74 John Herschel, "Catalogue of Nebulae and Clusters of Stars", *PT*, cliv (1864), 1–137.

75 J. L. E. Dreyer, "A New General Catalogue of Nebulae and Stars", *Memoirs of the RAS*, xlix (1888).

76 WH, *op. cit.* (ref. 25), 498–9.

77 *Chr*, 336, citing *Life and Letters of Th. Campbell*, ed. by W. Beattie (London, 1849).

*Index of Names**

*Other than members of the Herschel family